'ALL OF THE ESTABLISHMENTS
ARE OF THE HIGHEST CALIBRE ...
IT'S THE BEST GUIDE TO DINING
IN THE SOUTH WEST.'

SIMON HULSTONE

THE
TRENCHERMAN'S
GUIDE

TOP RESTAURANTS IN THE SOUTH WEST

Salt Media, 5 Cross Street, Devon, EX31 1BA.
www.saltmedia.co.uk
Tel: 01271 859299.
Email: info@saltmedia.co.uk

Design by Salt Media
Edited by Jo Rees
Cover image by: Kate Whitaker/Fifteen Cornwall.
Previous spread: cooking the launch lunch of the 22nd
edition at ABode Exeter/Guy Harrop.
Big salute to South West photographers David Griffen
and Guy Harrop who created many of the stunning
images featured in this year's guide.

The Trencherman's Guide is supported by

Bookatable♥

TotalProduce
Let's Grow Together

GIDLEIGH PARK p.88

FOREWORD

Welcome to the 23rd edition of The Trencherman's Guide, the South West's most prestigious guide to the best dining experiences from Cornwall to the Cotswolds.

Each year, the Trencherman's team at Salt Media prides itself on taking the guide a step further. This year's developments include easier to use navigation of the restaurants in each area, as well as an increased number of beautiful images, displaying the exquisite food and stylish restaurants in all their delicious, lip-smacking glory.

This year we launched the first ever Trencherman's Awards, and the guide's readers and Trencherman's Club members voted in their thousands for their favourite Trencherman's restaurant, chef, foodie hotel, front of house team, for the Trencherman's establishment that's demonstrated extraordinary creativity and innovation, and for the best newcomer to the guide. The results were announced at a fabulous dinner at Zacry's restaurant at Watergate Bay in Cornwall (see the pictures, left) and you'll find the winning establishments highlighted throughout the book.

I hope you find this year's guide a portal to some fabulous foodie adventures.

Enjoy!

Jo Rees
Editor, food Insider's Guides

Images from The Trencherman's Awards night, clockwise from top left: Neil Haydock in his kitchen at Zacry's, Michael Caines and *The Trencherman's Guide* ed Jo Rees, Zacry's front of house team, Trencherman's chefs Anton Piotrowski and Mark Dodson, dinner and interior at Zacry's, canapés by Louise McCrimmon.

IN THE GUIDE.

THE PILGRIMS RESTAURANT p.56

12 Welcome by Michael Caines

14 Join the club

16 Trencherman's: the movie

18 Using the guide

20 Gloucestershire

28 Wiltshire

40 Bath and Bristol

52 Somerset

62 Dorset and Hampshire

72 Devon

98 Cornwall

128 Index

WELCOME

After last year's good summer, and the easing up of the recession, we're heading into an exciting new era of top quality dining in the South West.

New restaurants are opening, young chefs are coming through and there are opportunities popping up every day.

With consumers increasingly viewing the South West as an exceptional food destination, we chefs are feeling buoyant and confident in developing the dining scene further. Nathan Outlaw relocating his restaurant to Port Isaac and my involvement with Kentisbury Grange in North Devon are both examples of this enthusiasm.

And nothing showcases what's going on in the South West dining scene as successfully as *The Trencherman's Guide*. For 23 years it's given food lovers the definitive list of must-visit West Country restaurants that reach the highest standards of cooking, service and dining experience, and which are invited into the guide on meeting a strict criteria.*

The group of leading chefs who are members of *The Trencherman's Guide* are a reflection of a vibrant food community which extends beyond the kitchen to our excellent local food and drink producers, and of course, to you, the reader.

I hope you enjoy this year's guide, and use it to discover wonderful food experiences in this beautiful part of the world.

Michael Caines MBE

Two Michelin-starred chef and chairman of *The Trencherman's Guide* editorial board

*Restaurants are invited to be in the guide on the basis of consistently high ratings across a selection of top international publications including the *Michelin Guide*, the *Good Food Guide* and the *AA Restaurant Guide*.

JOIN THE CLUB

The Trencherman's Club is a great way to find out about exclusive offers, special events and news from restaurants in the guide.

It's free and you'll get a fortnightly e-newsletter, plus access to events and the chance to vote in the Trencherman's Awards.

On the web

Find the full list of restaurants, read the latest features and book online at many of the restaurants in the guide on the website:
www.trenchermans-guide.com

Twitter and Facebook

Join the conversation on
Twitter: **@trenchermans**
Facebook: **The Trencherman's Guide**

On your tablet

Download the guide from **iTunes**,
Google Play and **www.pocketmags.com**

To be part of the South West's most exciting dining scene, join the club at:

www.trenchermans-guide.com

TRENCHERMAN'S
THE MOVIE

A number of the South West's leading chefs took part in the new Trencherman's film, *The A to Z of Dining*, that we made in the autumn with Wax Films. Look out for appearances from Michael Caines, Gordon Jones, Neil Haydock, Mark Dodson, Louise McCrimmon and Chris Cleghorn among others.

You can watch it on YouTube and at
www.trenchermans-guide.com/a-to-z-of-dining-trenchermans-guide-video

ING THE GUIDE

ZACRYS p.109

Some restaurants in the guide are accompanied by pictures and more information. These are Trencherman's establishments that have reached a higher level in the scoring criteria. All Trencherman's restaurants must meet a very high standard to be included, so they all offer an exceptional dining experience.

Special places to stay

The Trencherman's Guide has always included restaurants with rooms. Nowadays you'll find a good number of hotels with excellent restaurants among them, and you can identify places where you can dine and stay using this symbol.

Trencherman's Awards finalists

Trencherman's members who won a 2015 Trencherman's Award are celebrated in a series of full pages throughout the guide. You can identify finalists in each category by looking for this symbol at the top of the page.

GLOUCESTERSHIRE

Take a gastro tour of some of England's most delightful countryside, or head to town for smart dining.

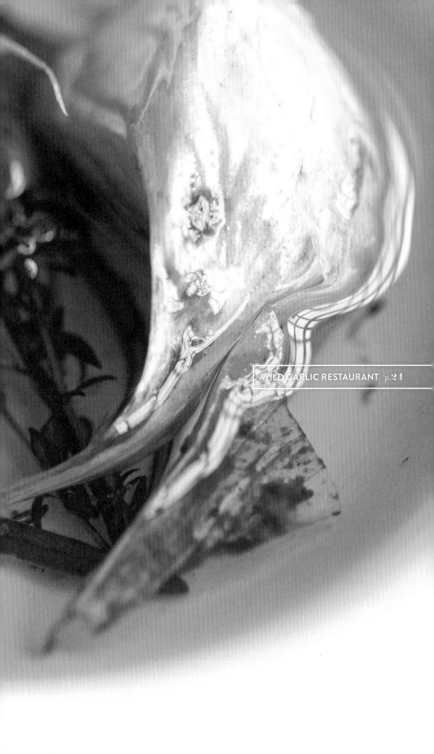

WILD GARLIC RESTAURANT p.21

Gloucestershire

1 Lower Slaughter Manor
2 The Slaughters Country Inn
3 Lumière
4 Wild Garlic Restaurant
5 mark@street
6 The Daffodil Restaurant
7 The Miners Country Inn

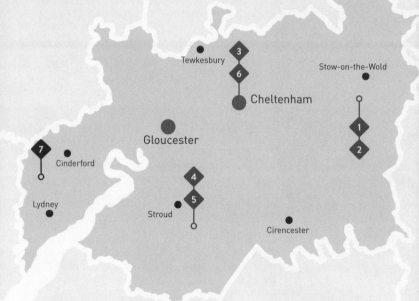

New in the guide this year:
mark@street and The Miners Country Inn.

Restaurants listed in the guide correspond to the numbers plotted on the map.
Locations are approximate.

1 $

Lower Slaughter Manor

EXQUISITE DINING AT THE MANOR

Situated in one of England's prettiest villages, Lower Slaughter Manor is a beautiful 17th century manor house which combines striking interiors with traditional charm, attentive service and one of the most acclaimed restaurants in the Cotswolds. Proud to be awarded three AA rosettes, the restaurant at Lower Slaughter Manor celebrates the finest regional and seasonal produce. Executive chef Nik Chappell creates tantalising menus that are English to their core and perfectly matched by the sommelier's exquisite wine selection.

Chef: **Nik Chappell**
3 course lunch from: **£25.50**
3 course dinner from: **£65**
Seats: **38**
Bedrooms: **19**
Room rate from: **£185**

Lower Slaughter, Gloucestershire, GL54 2HP.

T: **01451 820456**
E: **info@lowerslaughter.co.uk**
www.lowerslaughter.co.uk

f Lower Slaughter Manor
y @lowerslaughter

2 $

The Slaughters Country Inn

EXCEPTIONAL FOOD IN A COTSWOLD INN

Just a little way from its sister establishment, Lower Slaughter Manor, The Slaughters Country Inn offers the authentic charm of a traditional village inn – with exceptional food. Use of the best local produce, a fine selection of local ales, roaring log fires to warm the winter months and a stunning terrace for when the sun shines – this inn ticks all the boxes. Head chef Chris Fryer creates delicious dishes, simply prepared, using the finest Cotswold ingredients with menu items ranging from innovative dishes such as roast sea bream with lemon, chorizo, sorrel and butterbean stew, to more traditional country inn fare that's as comforting as the crackle of the fireplace.

Chef: **Chris Fryer**
3 course lunch from: **£25.25**
3 course dinner from: **£25.25**
Seats: **38**
Bedrooms: **30**
Room rate from: **£85**

Lower Slaughter, Gloucestershire, GL54 2HS.

T: **01451 822143**
E: **info@theslaughtersinn.co.uk**
www.theslaughtersinn.co.uk

f The Slaughters Country Inn
y @slaughtersinn

3
Lumière

CHELTENHAM'S CONTEMPORARY HIDDEN TREASURE

A discreet exterior belies the bold and exciting food offering at this restaurant in the centre of Regency Cheltenham. In 2009, after working for a number of Michelin-starred restaurants, chef Jon Howe and his wife Helen took over Lumière. Their first solo restaurant, it's become a showcase for Jon's unique culinary style. Everything is made in-house and he uses complex flavours to constantly create new and inventive takes on classic dishes. The couple's passion for food is reflected in Jon's thirst for new culinary discoveries and in the attention to detail that surrounds the Lumière dining experience. An intimate dining room, with mirrors and candles, creates a perfect contemporary atmosphere and the small team clearly shares Jon and Helen's excitement and dedication.

Chef: **Jon Howe**
3 course lunch from: **£28**
3 course dinner from: **£55**
Seats: **24**

Clarence Parade, Cheltenham, Gloucestershire, GL50 3PA.
T: 01242 222200
E: info@lumiere.cc
www.lumiere.cc

Lumière Restaurant Cheltenham
@lumierechelt

4 $ □
Wild Garlic Restaurant

INVENTIVE WAYS WITH LOCAL PRODUCE

This family run restaurant has become a Cotswold foodie destination thanks to chef-patron Matthew Beardshall's playful and inventive cooking. His menus showcase seasonal produce from the surrounding Five Valleys, and a strong focus on sustainability pervades. Eat in the refreshingly contemporary dining room and revel with the regulars in the six course tasting menu with matched wines that changes each month. For a more laid-back experience, try the restaurant's new tapas bar, which serves a selection of classic and modern tapas dishes and cocktails. Then complete the experience with a stay in one of three boutique bedrooms.

Chef: **Matthew Beardshall**
3 course lunch from: **£25**
3 course dinner from: **£25**
Seats: **29**
Bedrooms: **3**
Room rate from: **£95**

3 Cossack Square, Nailsworth, Gloucestershire, GL6 0DB.
T: 01453 832615
E: info@wild-garlic.co.uk
www.wild-garlic.co.uk

Wild Garlic Restaurant & Rooms
@thewildgarlic

GLOUCESTERSHIRE

LOWER SLAUGHTER MANOR p.23

5

mark@street

NEIGHBOURHOOD RESTAURANT WITH FLAIR IN NAILSWORTH

A relaxed, modern restaurant with candlelit tables, mark@street is tucked away on one of Nailsworth's side streets, the secluded location adding to its charm, which so many come here for. Chef-patron Mark Payne uses local ingredients which shine in his seasonal and contemporary approach to cookery. Dining here also has an entertaining element of surprise as the five course tasting menu remains a mystery to diners until the plates reach the table. Vegetables, soft fruits and herbs come fresh from Mark's allotment, and what he hasn't grown himself is sourced from the best local suppliers.

Chef: **Mark Payne**
3 course lunch from: **£21**
3 course dinner from: **£28.50**
Seats: **24**

Market Street, Nailsworth,
Gloucestershire, GL6 0BX.
T: 01453 839251
E: info@marketstreetnailsworth.co.uk
www.marketstreetnailsworth.co.uk

🅕 Mark@street
🐦 @markatstreet

6

The Daffodil Restaurant

ART DECO GRANDEUR IN CHELTENHAM

A contender for one of the most impressive dining rooms in the South West, The Daffodil is a restored 1920s picture house. Cinema seats have made way for dining tables and the former screen area is now an open plan kitchen where you can watch the team at work. There's art deco grandeur everywhere and the Circle Bar on the first floor is a perfect place to see the action while sipping a cocktail. The surroundings don't detract from the food however, which is classic and unpretentious. Leading the culinary operation is head chef Tom Rains whose experience includes working at Claridge's L'Escargot and as sous chef for Anton Mosimann. Open on Sundays for the first time this year.

Chef: **Tom Rains**
3 course lunch from: **£15.95**
3 course dinner from: **£30.95**
Seats: **120**

18-20 Suffolk Parade, Cheltenham,
Gloucestershire, GL50 2AE.
T: 01242 700055
E: eat@thedaffodil.com
www.thedaffodil.com

🅕 The Daffodil
🐦 @thedaffodil

GLOUCESTERSHIRE

7

The Miners Country Inn

Husband and wife team Steve and Sam Jenkins are fast making their pub the go-to spot in the Forest of Dean for quality food at excellent value. Ingredients are given proper attention, so there's six hour slow-cooked old spot pork belly and 32-day hung steak on the daily changing menu. Sourcing produce from the surrounding countryside, the team is always hunting for undiscovered foodie gems and was awarded a silver Taste of the West in 2014 to go with its AA rosette. The traditional pub feel is matched by the warm welcome.

Chef: **Steven Jenkins**. 3 course lunch from: **£14.95**. 3 course dinner from: **£14.95**. Seats: **60**. Bedrooms: **4**. Room rate from: **£50**

Chepstow Road, Sling, Coleford, Gloucestershire, GL16 8LH.

T: 01594 836632
E: admin@theminerssling.co.uk
www.theminerssling.co.uk

f The Miners Sling
y @theminerssling

GLOUCESTERSHIRE

INSIDER'S TIP

'For true indulgence I'd head to The Manor House (p 31) in Castle Combe or a perfect time in Cheltenham would have to involve cocktails at The Daffodil (p 26), then Jon's wonderful cooking at Lumiere (p 24).'

Matthew Beardshall, Wild Garlic Restaurant p.24

WILTSHIRE

Live it up in style at a grand country house or rough it with seriously good food and wine at a rural dining pub.

THE MANOR HOUSE p.**31**

Wiltshire

8   The Pear Tree at Purton
9   The Manor House
10 Lucknam Park Hotel and Spa
11 The Methuen Arms
12 The Harrow at Little Bedwyn
13 The George & Dragon
14 The Three Gables
15 The Foxham Inn
16 The Castle Inn Hotel

17 Brasserie at Lucknam Park Hotel & Spa
18 The Bell at Ramsbury
19 The Northey Arms
20 The Muddy Duck
21 The Fox at Broughton Gifford
22 The Longs Arms
23 The Three Daggers
24 Howard's House

New in the guide this year:
The Harrow at Little Bedwyn, The Pear Tree at Purton, The George & Dragon,
The Muddy Duck and The Three Daggers.

Restaurants listed in the guide correspond to the numbers plotted on the map.
Locations are approximate.

8 💲
The Pear Tree at Purton

WINE AND WILDFLOWERS IN A STUNNING HOTEL SETTING

This small, family run country house hotel is a former vicarage in the beautiful setting of seven and a half acres of grounds that include formal gardens, wildflower meadows with beehives and a vineyard. The restaurant is housed in a sunny conservatory and alongside the modern English menu, you'll find the Pear Tree's own Cuvee Alix white and Cuvee Anne sparkling wines. It's a perfect spot for a leisurely evening meal, but there's also the option of lunch, Sunday lunch and afternoon tea. With 17 bedrooms, it's a lovely place to visit for a gourmet break.

Chef: **Adam Conduit**
3 course lunch from: **£20**
3 course dinner from: **£30**
Seats: **48**
Bedrooms: **17**
Room rate from: **£109**

Church End, Purton, near Swindon, Wiltshire, SN5 4ED.
T: **01793 772100**
E: **stay@peartreepurton.co.uk**
www.peartreepurton.co.uk

The Pear Tree at Purton
@purtonpeartree

9 💲
The Manor House

COTSWOLD ESCAPE WITH MICHELIN-STARRED DINING

Set in one of the prettiest villages in England, The Manor House, an Exclusive Hotel & Golf Club, is surrounded by 365 acres of stunning Cotswold grounds. It's a magical 14th century building which has 48 individually designed rooms and suites alongside its Michelin-starred Bybrook Restaurant. At the helm is talented chef Richard Davies, who uses high quality ingredients to produce his beautiful dishes. This is indeed a picturesque place to dine and stay - you'll be transported to another era in the spacious lounges, open fireplaces and elegant décor. Guests can also work up an appetite for dinner on the award winning 18 hole golf course designed by Peter Alliss.

Chef: **Richard Davies**
3 course lunch from: **£30**
3 course dinner from: **£62**
Seats: **70**
Bedrooms: **48**
Room rate from: **£215**

Castle Combe, near Bath, Wiltshire, SN14 7HR.
T: **01249 784809**
E: **enquiries@manorhouse.co.uk**
www.manorhouse.co.uk

The Manor House Hotel and Golf Club
@themanorhouse

Lucknam Park Hotel and Spa

MICHELIN-STARRED DINING IN AN EXQUISITE MANSION HOUSE

Expectations are set high on arrival at this fabulous Palladian mansion, after travelling along the stately, mile-long tree-lined drive. Set in 500 acres of parkland, just six miles from Bath, this is an elegant hotel and spa with a Michelin-starred restaurant that also boasts five AA rosettes. The dining experience begins with cocktails and canapes in the drawing room or library before heading through to dinner in the Park Restaurant. Executive chef Hywel Jones – named Best Chef in the 2015 *Food* Reader Awards – uses organic ingredients and herbs from the hotel garden to create stunning dishes that are full of flavour. For dedicated foodies, there's also a cookery school onsite.

Chef: **Hywel Jones**
3 course lunch from: **£39 Sunday lunch**
3 course dinner from: **£80**
Seats: **64**
Bedrooms: **42**
Room rate from: **£275**

Colerne, Chippenham, Wiltshire, SN14 8AZ.
T: **01225 742777**
E: **reservations@lucknampark.co.uk**
www.lucknampark.co.uk
 Lucknam Park Hotel & Spa
 @lucknampark

The Methuen Arms

COMFORTABLE DINING PUB WITH ROOMS

This is a beautifully restored Georgian building, with wooden floorboards, rugs, exposed stone walls and log fires creating an atmospheric and cosy setting. It has several eating areas, from the snug to an alfresco dining space, and a lively bar which serves local real ales. The emphasis is on well sourced, simple food with value-for-money British and European influenced dishes that taste superb, while the owners, Martin and Debbie Still, ensure it's served in a relaxed and homely environment. Being not far from Bath, it's also a good base from which to explore the charming city and surrounding Wiltshire and Somerset countryside.

Chef: **Piero Boi**
3 course lunch from: **£18.50**
3 course dinner from: **£21.50**
Seats: **80**
Bedrooms: **14**
Room rate from: **£90**

2 High Street, Corsham, Wiltshire, SN13 0HB.
T: **01249 717060**
E: **info@themethuenarms.com**
www.themethuenarms.com
 The Methuen Arms
 @methuenarms

WILTSHIRE

12

The Harrow at Little Bedwyn

MICHELIN-STARRED COOKING IN A MODERN COUNTRY RESTAURANT

Holding a Michelin star for the ninth year running, it's no surprise to find superb food at this elegant brick building on the corner of a little lane in a Wiltshire village. Roger and Sue Jones are the husband and wife team behind the operation, of which every aspect has been expertly crafted – including an impressive and highly acclaimed wine list. Clever combinations bring an element of surprise to the menu, elevating the dining experience to another level. Food is sourced from an impressive list of artisan growers and producers of free range, quality ingredients – including regular supplies from chef Roger's own truffle hunting expeditions. Be tempted by the excellent value £40 tasting menu.

Chef: **Roger Jones**
3 course lunch from: **£40**
3 course dinner from: **£50**
Seats: **34**

High Street, Little Bedwyn, Marlborough, Wiltshire, SN8 3JP.
T: **01672 870871**
E: **office@theharrowatlittlebedwyn.com**
www.theharrowatlittlebedwyn.com

 The Harrow at Little Bedwyn
 @littlebedwyn

13 $

The George & Dragon

CORNISH SEAFOOD IN A HISTORIC WILTSHIRE PUB

This 15th century coaching inn has been thoughtfully refurbished to show off its historic credentials, with comfortable wooden tables, a snug bar and large inglenook fireplace where ten bottoms can snuggle up for a chat over a pint of real ale or glass of fine wine. With the same owners for ten years, the reputation of The George & Dragon has consistently grown and earned it two AA rosettes and an *Egon Ronay* star. Eat in the restaurant or the bar from a menu that specialises in seafood delivered daily from St Mawes in Cornwall. Three attractive country style bedrooms offer guests the chance to stay the night. Open seven days a week (closed Sunday night).

WILTSHIRE

Chefs: **Christopher Day and Tom Bryant**
3 course lunch from: **£19.50**
3 course dinner from: **£19.50**
Seats: **40**
Bedrooms: **3**
Room rate from: **£75**

High Street, Rowde, Devizes, Wiltshire, SN10 2PN.
T: **01380 723053**
E: **thegandd@tiscali.co.uk**
www.thegeorgeanddragonrowde.co.uk

Discover restaurants you love in the South West with

Bookatable ♡

Unrivalled Choice

Enjoy dining at top gastropubs, Michelin-starred venues, or celebrity chef restaurants.

Trusted Reviews

Read thousands of verified diner reviews to help you find the top rated places to eat.

Exceptional Offers

View hand-picked offers and recommended menus at top restaurants across the South West.

www.bookatable.co.uk

DOWNLOAD THE FREE BOOKATABLE APP

14

The Three Gables

A TASTE OF THE MED IN RURAL WILTSHIRE

Classically trained chef Marc Salmon and restaurant manager Vito Scaduto have put their years of experience into transforming this historic stone building into a fabulous restaurant. Their mission has been to take exceptional regional produce and use it to create modern menus packed with Mediterranean flavours and inspiration. Relax in the lounge bar or enjoy the elegant upstairs restaurant. Wherever you are in this stunning restaurant, you'll discover exceptional cuisine with very personal care and attention to detail.

INSIDER'S TIP

'Wales comes to Wiltshire in the guise of three Welsh Michelin-starred chefs: Hywel Jones at Lucknam Park (p 32), Richard Davies at The Manor House (p 31) and me at The Harrow at Little Bedwyn!'

Chef: **Marc Salmon**
3 course lunch from: **£18.50**
3 course dinner from: **£32.50**
Seats: **50**

Roger Jones, The Harrow at Little Bedwin. p.33

1 St Margaret's Street, Bradford on Avon, Wiltshire, BA15 1DA.
T: 01225 781666
E: info@thethreegables.com
www.thethreegables.com

🐦 @thethreegables

15

The Foxham Inn

Neil and Sarah Cooper run their pub with all the passion and commitment it takes to create a popular village local, including an imaginative approach to food. A genuine back to basics, homemade approach to all they do shines throughout this friendly country inn. Neil's extensive cheffing background means the well priced food is served with skill and flair, using ingredients such as Dorset snails, locally shot roe deer and Cornish seafood. The team is also keen to adapt dishes to suit individual diets and allergies - whether it's fish and chips with a gluten-free batter or its famed soya milk and raspberry crème brûlée.

Chef: **Neil Cooper**. 3 course lunch from: **£18**. 3 course dinner from: **£24**. Seats: **60**. Bedrooms: **2**. Room rate from: **£75 (single)**

Foxham, Chippenham, Wiltshire, SN15 4NQ.

T: 01249 740665
E: thefoxhaminn@hotmail.co.uk
www.thefoxhaminn.co.uk

The Foxham Inn
@thefoxhaminn

WILTSHIRE

16

The Castle Inn Hotel

This stunning Cotswold stone inn is situated in one of the prettiest villages in England and can trace its origins back to the 12th century. Having recently undergone an extensive – and sympathetic – restoration, many features from the original construction remain today. The hub of the inn is the bar with its open fire, warm atmosphere and table service, which serves traditional bar meals during the day and an à la carte menu in the evening. In warm weather, head to the terrace patio and for more intimate or private dining, the elegant Oak Room is the one to pick.

Chef: **Alex Ferguson**. 3 course lunch from: **£18.55**. 3 course dinner from: **£20.95**. Seats: **48**. Bedrooms: **11**. Room rate from: **£80**

Castle Combe, Chippenham, Wiltshire, SN14 7HN.

T: 01249 783030
E: enquiries@castle-inn.info
www.castle-inn.info

The Castle Inn Hotel - Castle Combe
@castleinnccombe

17 $

Brasserie at Lucknam Park Hotel & Spa

Stylish and contemporary, the Brasserie restaurant is situated in stunning Lucknam Park Hotel & Spa, six miles from Bath. In warm weather, dine alfresco on the pretty terrace overlooking the walled gardens and dovecote, or on cool days cosy up inside with a relaxed lunch in this beautiful setting. The open kitchen and wood-burning oven provide theatre as Michelin-starred executive chef Hywel Jones prepares varied and creative dishes for the interesting menus.

Chefs: **Hywel Jones and Ben Taylor**. 3 course lunch from: **£22**. 3 course dinner from: **£30**. Seats: **44**. Bedrooms: **42**. Room rate from: **£275**

Colerne, Chippenham, Wiltshire, SN14 8AZ.

T: 01225 742777
E: reservations@lucknampark.co.uk

www.lucknampark.co.uk

 Lucknam Park Hotel & Spa
@lucknampark

18 $

The Bell at Ramsbury

A walled kitchen garden provides chef Duncan Jones with plenty of inspiration for the dishes he serves in this 300-year-old former coaching inn. He also uses game from the Ramsbury Estate for his inspired menu. Alongside the more formal restaurant, there's the option of classic pub food, which you can enjoy with a pint of The Bell's own award winning beer. There's a busy cafe serving homemade cakes and a lovely garden to dine in throughout the summer - and if you want to hang around and explore the area, The Bell has nine beautifully furnished rooms.

Chef: **Duncan Jones**. 3 course lunch from: **£21**. 3 course dinner from: **£25**. Seats: **42 in restaurant and 28 in bar**. Bedrooms: **9**. Room rate from: **£110**

The Square, Ramsbury, Wiltshire, SN8 2PE.

T: 01672 520230
E: thebell@thebellramsbury.com

www.thebellramsbury.com

The Bell at Ramsbury
@thebellramsbury

19 $

The Northey Arms

Not far from Bath in the historic village of Box is the recently renovated Northey Arms. After a much needed revival, the newly modernised inn has been transformed into a popular place to eat, drink and stay. Ales and wines are specially selected so that the standard of what's in the glass matches the quality of the food on the plate. Along with the main menu which changes each season, there's an exclusive steak menu with a range of cuts sourced from the local butcher.

Chef: **Chris Alderson**. 3 course lunch from: **£26**. 3 course dinner from: **£28**. Seats: **70**. Bedrooms: **5**. Room rate from: **£105**

Bath Road, Box, Bath, Wiltshire, SN13 8AE.

T: 01225 742333
E: thenorthey@ohhcompany.co.uk

www.ohhpubs.com

The Northey Arms, Box, Wiltshire
@OHHpubs

20 $

The Muddy Duck

A modern take on the classic country inn, The Muddy Duck in Monkton Farleigh is the perfect place to escape the city. Situated on the outskirts of Bath, the award winning pub matches the warm and welcoming atmosphere of a rural inn with high standards of contemporary dining. The spacious pub has intimate areas for every sort of visit, whether you're looking to cosy up by the fire with a local ale and a few nibbles, or sample the seasonally inspired menu in the formal restaurant.

Chef: **Josh Roberts**. 3 course lunch from: **£18**. 3 course dinner from: **£25**. Seats: **45**. Bedrooms: **5**. Room rate from: **£120**

42 Monkton Farleigh, Bradford on Avon, Wiltshire, BA15 2QH.

T: 01225 858705
E: dishitup@themuddyduckbath.co.uk

www.themuddyduckbath.co.uk

The Muddy Duck, Monkton Farleigh
@muddyduckbath

WILTSHIRE

21
The Fox at Broughton Gifford

LIVE OFF THE FAT OF THE LAND AT THIS BEGUILING COUNTRY INN

It's easy to sink into the comfy leather sofas and stay awhile at this friendly Wiltshire pub. Wafts of baking bread will tempt, as will the range of local beers and malt whiskies on offer. The team here cares deeply about where its produce comes from, and it shows. Food is seasonal and simple, and there's a great use of its garden ingredients. The Fox even has a herd of pigs, meaning sausages, charcuterie, air-cured hams and bacon feature strongly on the menu. Accommodation is available across the road at the pub's swishly converted 200-year-old chapel called the Reading Room.

Chef: **Chris Hulbert**. 3 course lunch from: **£19.95**. 3 course dinner from: **£33**. Seats: **46**

The Street, Broughton Gifford, Melksham, Wiltshire, SN12 8PN.
T: 01225 782949
E: thefoxbroughton@gmail.com
www.thefoxbroughton.co.uk

f The Fox at Broughton Gifford
𝕏 @thefoxbroughton

The Longs Arms

With fine food, cask ales and years of rustic charm worn into the woodwork, The Longs Arms has everything you could ask for from a classic country pub. In his small but thoughtfully crafted menu, head chef and landlord Rob Allcock uses seasonal ingredients to piece together simple yet intriguing dishes. There's a lovely walled garden tucked behind the pub which overlooks the village's medieval church. It's a great spot to enjoy long summer evenings with a glass of something crisp and white from the wine list.

Chef: **Robert Allcock**. 3 course lunch from: **£28**. 3 course dinner from: **£28**. Seats: **36**

South Wraxall, Bradford on Avon, Wiltshire, BA15 2SB.

T: 01225 864450
E: info@thelongsarms.com
www.thelongsarms.com

The Longs Arms
@thelongsarms

23

The Three Daggers

Since re-opening in 2010 following extensive refurbishments, The Three Daggers has thrived as a village inn and must-visit foodie destination. The commitment to honest, local fare shines through its menu, with most produce seasonal and locally sourced – including from its own farm. The popular Sunday lunch menu is best served with a pint of ale from the on-site brewery. And don't go home without stocking up on fresh food and veg, homemade deli items, local cheeses, and beer, cider and wine at the farm shop.

Chef: **Dan Edgar**. 3 course lunch from: **£23**. 3 course dinner from: **£23**. Seats: **40**. Bedrooms: **3**. Room rate from: **£105**

47 Westbury Road, Edington, Westbury, Wiltshire, BA13 4PG.

T: 01380 830940
E: hello@threedaggers.co.uk
www.threedaggers.co.uk

The Three Daggers
@3daggers

24

Howard's House

There's a warm country welcome and plenty of personal touches to be found at this idyllic country hotel. The restaurant showcases British cookery at its best, with a distinctive menu from chef Nick Wentworth, who skilfully brings together simple ingredients to create outstanding dishes. There's also a daily special to reflect the best seasonal produce and an impressive wine list to choose from. A real retreat to escape from the city, Howard's House offers gourmet getaway packages too.

Chef: **Nick Wentworth**. 3 course lunch from: **£29.50**. 3 course dinner from: **£29.50**. Seats: **22**. Bedrooms: **9**. Room rate from: **£190**

Teffont Evias, Salisbury, Wiltshire, SP3 5RJ.

T: 01722 716392
E: enq@howardshousehotel.co.uk
www.howardshousehotel.co.uk

Howard's House Hotel
@howards_house

WILTSHIRE

BATH & BRISTOL

Head to the city for a blast of urban gastronomy from some exceptional chefs.

CASAMIA p.43

Bath & Bristol

25 Ronnie's of Thornbury
26 Casamia
27 Wilks Restaurant
28 Second Floor Restaurant and Bar
29 The Pump House
30 Bird in Hand
31 The Bath Priory
32 The Olive Tree Restaurant
33 Menu Gordon Jones
34 The Pony And Trap
35 The Wheatsheaf Combe Hay
36 Prego
37 The Kensington Arms
38 Graze Bar, Brewery and Chophouse
39 The Mint Room
40 Wheelwrights Arms

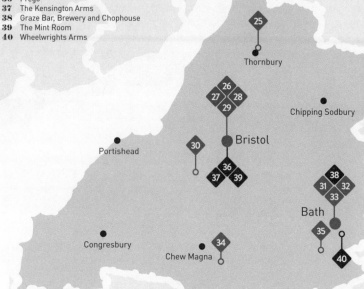

New in the guide this year:
The Wheatsheaf Combe Hay.

Restaurants listed in the guide correspond to the numbers plotted on the map.
Locations are approximate.

Ronnie's of Thornbury

EXCEPTIONAL FOOD ON THE OUTSKIRTS OF BRISTOL

Ronnie's is an exceptional restaurant; understated and set in a 17th century schoolhouse in the heart of the market town of Thornbury. Chef-owner Ron Faulkner was schooled in classic French techniques and worked the London fine dining circuit while perfecting his craft. Menus are built from seasonal produce, selected in their prime, and deeply rooted in a sound understanding of the classics. There's the option of tapas style dining in the bar. Creativity is always on show, but never overshadows the comfort factor. The wine list is concise, offering a selection of carefully crafted artisan wines from around the world, and guests can expect a warm welcome from the front of house team.

Chef: **Ron Faulkner**
3 course lunch from: **£13**
3 course dinner from: **£35**
Seats: **42 in restaurant, 30 in the bar**

11 St Mary Street, Thornbury, Bristol, BS35 2AB.

T: 01454 411137
E: info@ronnies-restaurant.co.uk
www.ronnies-restaurant.co.uk

Ronnie's of Thornbury
@ronniechef

Casamia

BROTHERS' DELICIOUS SEASONAL TASTING MENUS

Brothers Jonray and Peter Sanchez-Iglesias are behind this enchanting, Michelin-starred restaurant on the outskirts of Bristol. The chefs excite diners by combining simple, clean flavours with modern techniques to showcase an ingredient during the height of its season. You'll find locally driven dining that focuses on seasonal British produce, prepared in their open plan kitchen. There are set tasting menus for both lunch and dinner, and each is themed to the season, matched by changing restaurant décor. With a number of nostalgic memories influencing the food, the experience of tucking into these creative dishes feels intimate and special. There's also a Test Kitchen on site where the brothers develop ideas and share culinary secrets with fellow food lovers.

BATH & BRISTOL

Chef: **Jonray and Peter Sanchez-Iglesias**
5 course lunchtime tasting menu: **£38,** wine flight **£30**
10 course tasting menu: **£68,** wine flight **£60**
Seats: **40**

38 High Street, Westbury-on-Trym, Bristol, BS9 3DZ.

T: 0117 9592884
E: info@casamiarestaurant.co.uk
www.casamiarestaurant.co.uk

Casamia
@casamia_

Wilks Restaurant

GOING WILD AND LOCAL WITH A MICHELIN STAR

This neighbourhood restaurant opened in 2012 and quickly went on to earn its first Michelin star – thanks to the original cooking of chef-owner James Wilkins. Vibrant and stylish, it also offers excellent value for money. James spent years travelling and working extensively around the world before realising his dream of having his own restaurant. Inspired by his travel experiences, his unique dishes are simple and light yet packed with flavour. Keen to use as many wild foods as possible, he also champions all that's local – farmers, growers, suppliers – so it's no surprise he draws produce from a nearby walled garden. Check out the artwork too – from local artists of course.

Chef: **James Wilkins**
3 course lunch from: £23
3 course dinner from: £43
Seats: **30**

1 Chandos Road, Bristol, BS6 6PG.
T: **01179 737999**
E: **info@wilksrestaurant.co.uk**
www.wilksrestaurant.co.uk

f Wilks Restaurant
🐦 @wilksrestaurant

Second Floor Restaurant and Bar

MODERN BRITISH COOKING SERVED WITH AWARD WINNING STYLE

The Second Floor Restaurant at Harvey Nichols in the heart of Bristol city centre offers the very best in modern cooking, stylish surroundings and impeccable service. Leading the team is award winning executive chef Louise McCrimmon who takes huge pride in using the finest local and seasonal ingredients to create an eclectic selection of all-day dining menus, from breakfast right through to dinner. Each dish expertly combines classic techniques and indulgent tastes for seasonally changing specialities. The neighbouring Second Floor Bar, with its mouth-watering cocktail menu, is the perfect stop for an aperitif or post-dinner drinks.

Chef: **Louise McCrimmon**
3 course lunch from: £20
3 course dinner from: £20
Seats: **60**

27 Philadelphia Street, Quakers Friars, Bristol, BS1 3BZ.
T: **0117 9168898**
E: **reception.bristol@harveynichols.com**
www.harveynichols.com/restaurants

f Harvey Nichols
🐦 @hn_bristol

29
The Pump House

FABULOUS SEASONAL FOOD ON THE HARBOUR

This Victorian pumping station on Bristol's harbour features an informal downstairs dining area with an impressive bar, and a large outdoor terrace for drinks and dining. However, the most exciting bit is upstairs where a contemporary dining room is the setting for fabulous tasting menus, featuring ingredients foraged by chef Toby Gritten and team, and produce which is sourced as locally as possible. The result is an award winning, fine dining restaurant with a keen sense of the changing seasons. Choose from the five or eight course tasting menus and match with wines from an award winning list.

Chef: **Toby Gritten**
3 course lunch from: **£25**
3 course dinner from: **£30**
Seats: **40**

Merchants Road, Hotwells, Bristol, BS8 4PZ.

T: **01179 272229**
E: **info@the-pumphouse.com**
www.the-pumphouse.com

The Pump House
@pumphsebristol

30
Bird in Hand

FORAGERS' FIND IN BRISTOL

This is a seriously food-led pub which is all about offering an authentic modern British food experience using local and foraged produce. Situated close to central Bristol, but in a rural setting, this is a little gem with a big following. Gin lovers will revel in the huge list at the bar, while real ales and a carefully selected wine list also delight. A seasonal à la carte menu offers beautifully executed and thoughtfully designed dishes, and the Bird is also loved for its Sunday roasts. You can also eat from the lighter bar menu six days a week.

Chef: **Jack Williams**
3 course lunch from: **£20**
3 course dinner from: **£25**
Seats: **28**

17 Weston Road, Long Ashton, Bristol, BS41 9LA.

T: **01275 395222**
E: **info@bird-in-hand.co.uk**
www.bird-in-hand.co.uk

Bird In Hand
@birdinhand2011

The Bath Priory

MICHELIN-STARRED DINING AT THE ELEGANT PRIORY

Set within four acres of mature award-winning gardens, The Bath Priory is set apart as a peaceful haven in the bustling city. The late-Georgian stone mansion enjoys a tranquil location just a short walk through Royal Victoria Park to Bath's city centre – and proudly holds the only Michelin star in the centre for its exceptional cuisine. Executive chef Sam Moody offers a memorable culinary experience, with a focus on fresh local produce, flavour and balance in the creation of exciting, modern British dishes. The experience is completed with the dining room's views over the beautiful gardens.

Chef: **Sam Moody**
3 course lunch from: **£27.50**
3 course dinner from: **£80**
Seats: **60**
Bedrooms: **33**
Room rate from: **£210**

Weston Road, Bath, Somerset, BA1 2XT.

T: 01225 331922
E: info@thebathpriory.co.uk

www.thebathpriory.co.uk

 The Bath Priory Hotel, Restaurant & Spa
 @thebathpriory

The Olive Tree Restaurant

CREATIVE COOKING IN A QUIRKY BOUTIQUE HOTEL

The Olive Tree is one of Bath's best established culinary institutions and is led by highly accomplished and inventive chef Chris Cleghorn. It's at the heart of stylish boutique hotel The Queensberry, and reflects the hotel's quirky, private club-style atmosphere. Chris' experience of working with Michelin restaurant names like Michael Caines, Heston Blumenthal and Adam Simmonds shows in his incredible attention to detail and ability to draw out and combine the flavours of the ingredients he uses. His dishes are complex but also clean, fresh and refreshingly simple. With a superb wine list and top notch service, The Olive Tree has a well deserved three AA rosette rating and won Best Hotel in the 2015 *Food* Reader Awards.

Chef: **Chris Cleghorn**
3 course lunch from: **£25**
3 course dinner from: **£40**
Seats: **55**
Bedrooms: **29**
Room rate from: **£130**

The Queensberry Hotel, 4-7 Russel Street, Bath, Somerset, BA1 2QF.

T: 01225 447928
E: reservations@olivetreebath.co.uk

www.olivetreebath.co.uk

 Olive Tree
 @olivetreebath

33
Menu Gordon Jones

CREATIVITY AND INNOVATION GROUNDED IN SCOTTISH CULINARY ROOTS

There are two things you really need to know about Menu Gordon Jones – firstly, it won the Creativity and Innovation award in the 2015 Trencherman's Awards, and secondly – there's a long waiting list. Pre-booking is essential at this 20 cover restaurant, which is just a short stroll from Bath's city centre. The food cooked by Michelin-trained Gordon is breathtakingly beautiful and the incredible set menus will delight. There's always an element of surprise and eating here is an event – but it's grounded in the chef's Scottish, honest culinary roots. As Mr Jones himself says, 'Come with an open mind and enjoy the experience.'

BATH & BRISTOL

Chef: **Gordon Jones**. 5 course tasting lunch: **£40**. 6 course tasting dinner: **£55**. Seats: **20**

2 Wellsway, Bath, Somerset, BA2 3AQ.
T: **01225 480871**
E: info@menugordonjones.co.uk
www.menugordonjones.co.uk

@menugordonjones

34

The Pony & Trap

MICHELIN-STARRED DINING PUB FROM BROTHER AND SISTER TEAM

The multi-award winning sibling duo at the heart of this 200-year-old country pub have maintained a Michelin star since 2011 and continue to take the menu and the pub's reputation from strength to strength. Josh and Holly Eggleton lead a talented team, serving up food and drink from the very best growers and producers in the region. Local sourcing and sustainable food is central to their culinary ethos and their energy and commitment sees them working with a host of similarly minded local food and farming organisations. Whether it's a drink at the bar and simple pub lunch or the chance to experience the fabulous six course tasting menu – there's something special to be found, whatever the occasion.

Chef: **Josh Eggleton**
3 course lunch from: **£25**
3 course dinner from: **£30**
Seats: **60**

Knowle Hill, Chew Magna, Bristol, BS40 8TQ.

T: 01275 332627
E: info@theponyandtrap.co.uk
www.theponyandtrap.co.uk

f Pony and Trap
y @theponyandtrap

35 $

The Wheatsheaf Combe Hay

IMAGINATIVE COOKING IN THE COUNTRYSIDE

Just four miles outside of Bath, this popular dining pub is set in a picture-perfect countryside valley. Dating back to the 16th century, the former farmhouse-turned-pub is all rustic chic, with plenty of wood and stone and muted colours. Chef Eddy Rains turns out an impressive modern British menu, and he's not afraid to experiment. Cosy in the winter, this is also a stunning place to visit in the warmer months thanks to its tiered gardens that look out over the village and valley. You'll also appreciate the veg patch and beehives, which all add to the Wheatsheaf's charm. Three rooms in a converted cowshed allow for the opportunity to stay over – and you can even bring four-footed companions.

Chef: **Eddy Rains**
3 course lunch from: **£14.50**
3 course dinner from: **£26**
Seats: **55**
Bedrooms: **3**
Room rate from: **£120**

Combe Hay, Bath, Somerset, BA2 7EG.

T: 01225 833504
E: info@wheatsheafcombehay.com
www.wheatsheafcombehay.com

36
Prego

Real Italian food is the order of the day at Prego, a former shop turned restaurant in a suburban corner of Bristol. Opened in 2010 by brothers-in-law Julian Faiello and Olly Gallery, it's a huge hit with the locals. Chef Olly uses local produce and carefully sourced Italian artisan items to create regional Italian dishes. The handmade pasta and Neapolitan-style pizza are deservedly popular, and there's an inventive specials board which includes dishes like zappa di pesce with Cornish black bream or eight hour beef shin ragu, montepulciano and pappardelle.

Chef: **Olly Gallery**. 3 course lunch from: **£14**. 3 course dinner from: **£25**. Seats: **50**

7 North View, Westbury Park, Bristol, BS6 7PT.

T: 0117 9730496
E: info@pregobar.co.uk

www.pregobar.co.uk

@ollyprego1

BATH & BRISTOL

37
The Kensington Arms

The Kensington Arms is an independently owned pub and restaurant located in Redland, just a short walk from Bristol's vibrant Gloucester Road and Clifton Village. The focus is on simple, honest pub food with a commitment to quality – whether you're trying the homemade sausage roll bar snack or the roe deer supper dish. With the warm buzz of families, friends, dogs and children, you can expect a proper village pub vibe in the heart of a big city when you visit "The Kenny" – as it's affectionately known.

Chef: **Jan Ostle**. 3 course lunch from: **£20**. 3 course dinner from: **£22**. Seats: **38**

35-37 Stanley Road, Redland, Bristol, BS6 6NP.

T: 01179 446444
E: info@thekensingtonarms.co.uk

www.thekensingtonarms.co.uk

@kensingtonarms

38
Graze Bar, Brewery and Chophouse

Inspiration here comes from the inventiveness and pared-back simplicity of classic New York and London steak houses. Expect to discover modern British and European dishes in a large, contemporary space in the buzzing foodie quarter adjacent to Bath Spa station. Open from breakfast through to dinner, Graze has an open-plan kitchen and uses a Josper charcoal oven to do justice to its speciality meat dishes. The flagship restaurant for Bath Ales, it stocks an excellent selection of fine ales, wines, spirits and also houses its own microbrewery.

Chef: **Ben Morse**. 3 course lunch from: **£20**. 3 course dinner from: **£25**. Seats: **140**

9, Brunel Square, Bath, BA1 1SX.
T: 01225 429392
E: grazebath@bathales.co.uk
www.bathales.com

 Graze Bath
 @grazebath

39
The Mint Room

Modern and spacious, and super cool in decoration, the newly opened Mint Room Bristol has quickly established itself as one of the most interesting contemporary Indian restaurants outside London. Emulating the original Bath site, the restaurant uses a combination of high quality local and free range ingredients, which are transformed into vibrant, modern, regional Indian dishes by a team of experienced chefs backed up by knowledgeable front of house staff.

Chef: **Saravanan Nambirajan**. 3 course lunch/dinner from: **£25-£30**. Seats: **70**

12-16 Clifton Road, Clifton, Bristol, BS8 1AF.
T: 0117 3291300
E: info@themintroom.co.uk
www.themintroom.co.uk

 The Mint Room
 @themintroom

40
Wheelwrights Arms

The ideal country pub, the 18th century Wheelwrights Arms nestles in a little village just two miles from Bath city centre. Head chef Matthew Brooks creates seasonal food using locally sourced ingredients which is accompanied by an imaginative wine list, real ales and local cider. From Monday to Saturday there's also the option of booking a six course tasting menu for £35 a head. Sit outside in the large garden or cosy up inside next to the log fire. Seven stylish ensuite rooms await upstairs and the pub has its own car park.

Chef: **Matthew Brooks**. 3 course lunch from: **£13.50**. 3 course dinner from: **22**. Seats: **45**. Bedrooms: **7**. Room rate from: **£85**

Church Lane, Monkton Combe, Bath, BA2 7HB.
T: 01225 722287
E: bookings@wheelwrightarms.co.uk
www.wheelwrightarms.co.uk

 The Wheelwrights Arms
 @thewheelwrights

SOMERSET

From village dining pubs to dinner in the charming city of Wells, we celebrate the small but perfectly formed.

Somerset

41 The Swan
42 Goodfellows
43 The Pilgrims Restaurant
44 The White Hart
45 Augustus
46 The Castle at Taunton
47 The Queens Arms
48 Little Barwick House
49 Best Western Plus Centurion Hotel
50 Psalter's Restaurant at The Luttrell Arms
51 The Rising Sun Inn
52 The Globe
53 The White Horse

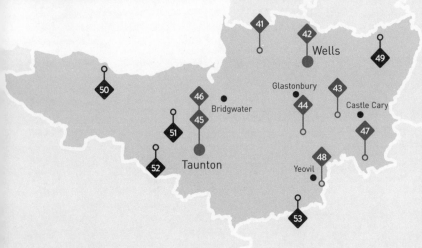

New in the guide this year:
Little Barwick House, The Globe, The Castle at Taunton, The White Horse,
Psalter's Restaurant at The Luttrell Arms.

Restaurants listed in the guide correspond to the numbers plotted on the map.
Locations are approximate.

41 ⬧

The Swan

CHIC FOODIE PUB IN A LIVELY SOMERSET VILLAGE

This vibrant foodie pub in the lively Somerset village of Wedmore is the result of a sensitive restoration of a neglected coaching inn. Elegant architectural details sit alongside modern, quirky décor, and it's a great place to pop in for coffee or a pint. However, food is key here, thanks to the direction of Tom Blake (formerly of River Cottage Canteen) and his wholesome, fresh and unfussy style of cooking. There are plenty of different areas to explore, from a cosy corner in the bar to the spacious dining room and peaceful garden. Seven ensuite bedrooms make it easy to stay a little longer.

Chef: **Rob Smart**
3 course lunch from: **£22**
3 course dinner from: **£22**
Seats: **80**
Bedrooms: **7**
Room rate from: **£85**

Cheddar Road, Wedmore, Somerset, BS28 4EQ.

T: **01934 710337**
E: **info@theswanwedmore.com**
www.theswanwedmore.com

f The Swan Wedmore
🐦 @theswanwedmore

42

Goodfellows

LOCALS' FAVOURITE IN CHARMING WELLS

Just a few steps away from beautiful Wells Cathedral, this is a neighbourhood restaurant that consistently turns out superb food. It's no surprise that it holds two AA rosettes for the high quality of head chef Adam Fellows' cooking. The open plan kitchen creates a relaxed and intimate theatre setting, offering diners the chance to watch all of the kitchen action captured on camera and displayed on flat screen TVs. Adam combines the best of Mediterranean cuisine with fish caught off the Devon and Cornwall coasts and top quality West Country produce, which has earned him a number of awards.

Chef: **Adam Fellows**
3 course lunch from: **£23.50**
3 course dinner from: **£30**
Seats: **35**

5 Sadler Street, Wells, Somerset, BA5 2RR.

T: **01749 673866**
E: **goodfellowseat@gmail.com**
www.goodfellowswells.co.uk

f Goodfellows Restaurant, Wells
🐦 @goodfellowseat

43 $

The Pilgrims Restaurant

DINE ON THE BOUNTY OF THE COUNTRYSIDE

It must be a labour of love when the chef spends his days off down country lanes searching out the very best local ingredients. But Jools Mitchison invests huge amounts of time uncovering the seasonal foodie delights that surround his Somerset restaurant. He then cooks them simply, allowing these top quality ingredients to shine. The rural theme is echoed in the tasteful, calm interior and genuine warm welcome at this restaurant with rooms. It's testament to Jools and his wife Sally's 20 years at The Pilgrims that they have a loyal band of happy diners who return to eat here again and again.

Chef: **Jools Mitchison**
3 course lunch from: **£26**
3 course dinner from: **£28**
Seats: **24**
Bedrooms: **5**
Room rate from: **£70**

Pilgrims Way, Lovington, Castle Cary, Somerset, BA7 7PT.
T: 01963 240600
E: jools@thepilgrimsatlovington.co.uk
www.thepilgrimsatlovington.co.uk

f The Pilgrims at Lovington
y @pilgrimskitchen

44 $

The White Hart

REFRESHING NEW CUISINE AT AN ANCIENT SOMERSET PUB

Inspired by his years at River Cottage Canteen, chef Tom Blake brings his refreshing culinary style to The White Hart. It's an ancient pub in the heart of Somerton, a quietly grand town with a rich history. The inn was lavishly restored two years ago by the team behind The Swan in Wedmore and, like its sister pub, it has a relaxed, arty vibe with food served from breakfast through to dinner. Tom's aim is to demonstrate the quality of West Country ingredients by serving fresh produce in simple, but special, dishes. There are also eight ensuite rooms, plus a courtyard and garden.

Chef: **Aimee Tinker**
3 course lunch from: **£22**
3 course dinner from: **£22**
Seats: **88**
Bedrooms: **8**
Room rate from: **£85**

Market Place, Somerton, Somerset, TA11 7LX.
T: 01458 272273
E: info@whitehartsomerton.com
www.whitehartsomerton.com

f The White Hart Inn
y @whitehartsom

LITTLE BARWICK HOUSE p.59

45

Augustus

RICHARD GUEST'S LAID BACK BISTRO

Locals in the know seek out this wonderful little restaurant which is tucked away in a courtyard in the centre of Taunton. Chef Richard Guest, previously of the nearby Castle Hotel, is doing great things in this solo venture, along with Cedric Chirossel at front of house. The relaxed, laid-back bistro approach at Augustus produces cooking that, for all its simple appearance, has the hidden depth of the chef's fine dining background. Expect unfussy dishes with French, English and Asian influences. There's a particularly good wine list too.

Chef: **Richard Guest**
3 course lunch from: **£25**
3 course dinner from: **£25**
Seats: **28**

3 The Courtyard, St James Street, Taunton, Somerset, TA1 1JR.

T: 01823 324354
E: info@augustustaunton.co.uk
www.augustustaunton.com

 Augustus Restaurant
 @augustustaunton

46 💲

The Castle at Taunton

A WEST COUNTRY INSTITUTION

With a history stretching back eight centuries, The Castle at Taunton is the West Country's most enduring watering hotel. The food has always been of note here, with a number of big name chefs heading the kitchen, and with Castle Bow, the raffish art deco-inspired restaurant, it maintains its excellent reputation. Head chef Liam Finnegan continues The Castle's long-held campaign to celebrate the 'Great' in British cooking. For informal dining, try its popular sister brasserie, BRAZZ, next door.

Chef: **Liam Finnegan**
3 course dinner from: **£34**
Seats: **36**
Bedrooms: **44**
Room rate from: **£99**

Castle Green, Taunton, Somerset, TA1 1NF.

T: 01823 328328
E: restaurant@the-castle-hotel.com
www.castlebow.com

 The Castle at Taunton
 @castletaunton

47 $

The Queens Arms

STYLISH VILLAGE INN WITH
FOOD FROM ITS OWN FARM

Situated at the foot of the rolling hills on the Dorset/Somerset border, the two AA rosette Queens Arms is the sort of village pub you dream of. A family run 18th century inn, it has bags of historic charm with its flagstone floors and rugs, excellent real ale options and warm welcome for muddy footed locals – both two- and four-legged varieties. It's also got a modern, arty feel and the eight bedrooms are tastefully stylish. Large amounts of restaurant produce come from the village itself, including the inn's own small, free range farm. Menus are cleverly balanced between classic pub food and imaginative restaurant dishes and you can eat in the cosy bar, out on the terrace, or in the light-filled dining room – which also doubles up as a cinema on film nights.

Chef: **Ben Abercrombie**
3 course lunch from: **£20.95**
3 course dinner from: **£30.95**
Seats: **78**
Bedrooms: **8**
Room rate from: **£85**

Corton Denham, Sherborne, Somerset, DT9 4LR.

T: 01963 220317
E: relax@thequeensarms.com

www.thequeensarms.com

f The Queens Arms Pub - Corton Denham, Somerset
y @queensarmspub

48 $

Little Barwick House

HIGH CLASS COOKING IN A FAMILY
RUN RESTAURANT WITH ROOMS

Entering its 16th season, Little Barwick House has established itself as one of the most consistent restaurants with rooms in the country. It's run by the Ford family and has held three AA rosettes since opening. Expect to find delicious, classically based dishes with a modern twist, served in an elegant, but relaxed, fine dining atmosphere. The extensive wine list is an important feature with many good wines available by the glass including Krug champagne. Awarded Editor's Choice Gourmet Hotel in the *2015 Good Hotel Guide* and the Fabulous Food Award by *Sawdays*.

Chefs: **Tim and Olly Ford**
3 course lunch from: **£29.95**
3 course dinner from: **£47.95**
Seats: **40**
Bedrooms: **6**
Room rate from: **£95**

Rexes Hollow Lane, Barwick, near Yeovil, Somerset, BA22 9TD.

T: 01935 423902
E: info@littlebarwick.co.uk

www.littlebarwickhouse.co.uk

f Little Barwick House
y @littlebarwick

SOMERSET

49

Best Western Plus Centurion Hotel

With its refurbished dining room and chef on a mission to create a stylish new dining experience, the Centurion is an appealing hotel choice for foodies. It's about 20 minutes south of Bath and boasts a spa, health club and nine hole parkland golf course. The Restaurant @ Centurion, which overlooks the gardens, has a contemporary feel and includes an elegant conservatory area. The friendly front of house team complements head chef Sean Horwood's confident menus, which make use of seasonal produce from local suppliers.

Chef: **Sean Horwood**. 3 course lunch from: **£20**. 3 course dinner from: **£27**. Seats: **60**. Bedrooms: **45**. Room rate from: **£85**

Charlton Lane, Midsomer Norton, Radstock, Somerset, BA3 4BD.

T: 01761 412214
E: enquiries@ centurionhotel.co.uk

www.centurionhotel.co.uk

f Best Western PLUS Centurion Hotel
🐦 @restatcent

50

Psalter's Restaurant at The Luttrell Arms

At the gateway to beautiful, wild Exmoor, Psalter's Restaurant is building a reputation not only for its game dishes, but also for its innovative seasonal food. The restaurant prepares dishes using local produce that's 100 per cent traceable, using minimal food miles. Whether you're staying in one of the 28 elegant ensuite bedrooms, dining at Psalter's or in the bar area, or even in the secret garden, you'll enjoy a memorable experience.

Chef: **Miguel Tenreiro**. 3 course lunch from: **£16.95**. 3 course dinner from: **£29**. Seats: **45**. Bedrooms: **28**. Room rate from: **£140**

The Luttrell Arms Hotel, 32-36 High Street, Dunster, Somerset, TA24 6SG.

T: 01643 821555
E: enquiry@luttrellarms.co.uk

www.luttrellarms.co.uk

f The Luttrell Arms Hotel
🐦 @psaltersdining

51 ⟳

The Rising Sun Inn

Cob walls, oak beams and a slate floor set
the scene at this a gorgeous old pub on the
edge of the Quantock Hills in Somerset to
which Jon and Christine Brinkman have
added their own individual touches, such
as art nouveau wall lights and rich fabrics.
There's a warm welcome as you enter through
the magnificent door to the bar area and
an upstairs dining gallery has views of the
surrounding countryside. From a light lunch to
a hearty dinner, it's an impressive setting for
high quality food.

Chef: **Kevin Webber, Jonathan Brinkman and
Tom Learmouth**. 3 course lunch from: **£25**.
3 course dinner from: **£35**. Seats: **65**

West Bagborough, Taunton, Somerset, TA4 3EF.

T: 01823 432575
E: jon@risingsuninn.info

www.risingsuninn.info

53

The White Horse

The White Horse is a 17th century former
coaching inn located in the charming village
of Haselbury Plucknett. This family run pub
combines fine dining with simple classic pub
food – from Dorset snail bourguignon to honey
roast ham with free range eggs and hand-cut
chips. Ingredients are locally sourced and
there's a wide range of real ales and exciting
wines on offer. Whether you're visiting for a
drink, a light lunch or a celebration, service
is consistently friendly and warm, as is the
environment. Cosy up by the fire in winter or
enjoy the pretty rose garden in summer.

Chef: **Richard Robinson**. 3 course lunch from:
£17.95. 3 course dinner from: **£17.95**. Seats: **35**

North Street, Haselbury Plucknett,
Somerset, TA18 7RJ.

T: 01460 78873
E: whitehorsehaselbury@hotmail.co.uk

www.thewhitehorsehaselbury.co.uk

 The White Horse

52 ⟳

The Globe

If there's nothing that makes you feel more
at home than a hearty meal and the warm
welcome of a traditional pub, then the family
run Globe at Milverton should tick all your
boxes. It's a contemporary pub serving
modern British food (the slow roasted belly
pork is a must) and has a relaxed, welcoming
style. Local ales and a well priced wine list
sit alongside the menu, which reflects a wide
range of Somerset produce. Enjoy the sun
terrace in the summer months.

Chefs: **Mark Tarry and Kaan Atasoy**. 3 course
lunch from: **£21**. 3 course dinner from: **£21**.
Seats: **45**. Bedrooms: **2**. Room rate from: **£55**

Fore Street, Milverton, near Taunton,
Somerset, TA4 1JX.

T: 01823 400534
E: info@theglobemilverton.co.uk

www.theglobemilverton.co.uk

 The Globe Milverton
 @infomilverton

INSIDER'S
TIP

'I've eaten at The Pony and
Trap (p 49) and Casamia
(p 43) in the last year and
both were excellent. Great food
and service, and some really
innovative dishes at Casamia.'

Adam Fellows, Goodfellows. Page 55.

DORSET & HAMPSHIRE

Seafood's the star on the Jurassic Coast, while inland,
cosy rural retreats are the order of the day.

HIGHCLIFF GRILL RESTAURANT p.67

Dorset & Hampshire

54 Best Western The Grange at Oborne
55 The Three Lions
56 Beaminster Brasserie at the BridgeHouse
57 Riverside Restaurant
58 Highcliff Grill Restaurant
59 The Stapleton Arms
60 The Fontmell
61 Acorn Inn
62 Hix Oyster and Fish House
63 Captains Club Hotel and Spa
64 WestBeach
65 Arbor Restaurant
66 Crab House Cafe

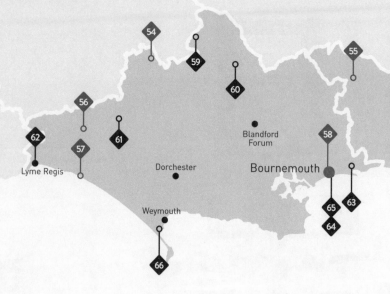

Lyme Regis

Dorchester

Blandford Forum

Bournemouth

Weymouth

New in the guide this year:
Captains Club Hotel and Spa.

Restaurants listed in the guide correspond to the numbers plotted on the map.
Locations are approximate.

54 💲

Best Western
The Grange at Oborne

CLASSIC DINING WITH
GARDEN VIEWS

The Grange at Oborne is a privately owned and family run country house hotel with a warm and relaxing restaurant that overlooks a beautiful floodlit garden to the rear of the hotel. Head chef Simon Clewlow works tirelessly to create delicious menus using fresh, local and seasonal produce, with the emphasis on taste and quality. Awarded gold by Taste Of The West in 2014.

Chef: **Simon Clewlow**
3 course lunch from: **£26**
3 course dinner from: **£35**
Seats: **45**
Bedrooms: **18**
Room rate from: **£99**

Oborne, Sherborne, Dorset, DT9 4LA.
T: **01935 813463**
E: **reception@thegrange.co.uk**
www.thegrangeatoborne.co.uk
◻ The Grange at Oborne
◻ @grangeatoborne

55 💲

The Three Lions

DESTINATION DINING –
WITH SAUNA AND WHIRLPOOL!

A family run English restaurant with rooms on the edge of the New Forest, featuring gardens, a sauna and a whirlpool. This destination dining pub with English/French cuisine has at its helm head chef Mike Womersley, who held a Michelin star for five years while at Lucknam Park. The intimate bar has an open log-burning fire and cosy conservatory meeting room. The Three Lions has a raft of awards to its name, including a four star Silver Award and Breakfast Award from VisitBritain and it's been named three times as Hampshire restaurant of the year in its 20 years of being in *The Good Food Guide*.

Chef: **Mike Womersley**
3 course lunch from: **£23.50**
3 course dinner from: **£29.50**
Seats: **60**
Bedrooms: **7**
Room rate from: **£40 per person per night**

Stuckton, Fordingbridge, Hampshire, SP6 2HF.
T: **01425 652489**
E: **the3lions@btinternet.com**
www.thethreelionsrestaurant.com

DORSET & HAMPSHIRE

56 💲

Beaminster Brasserie at the BridgeHouse

HEAVENLY FOOD IN A FORMER PRIEST'S HOUSE

Flanked by a walled garden and the River Brit, this 13th century former priest's house is a characterful, gorgeous stone building, which cleverly retains a strong sense of the past, while still feeling classy and modern. The food is equally appealing, and there's a choice of dining areas, from the chic Georgian dining room to the alfresco brasserie. Head chef Stephen Pielesz calls on his classical training to create modern British dishes, using produce from the Dorset countryside. Hospitality and friendliness is key, and Stephen even sometimes brings his dishes to diners' tables. Look out for his signature tongue-in-cheek All Day Snail Breakfast.

Chef: **Stephen Pielesz**
3 course lunch from: **£25**
3 course dinner from: **£40**
Seats: **45**
Bedrooms:**13**
Room rate from: **£95**

3 Prout Bridge, Beaminser, Dorset, DT8 3AY.
T: **01308 862200**
E: **enquiries@bridge-house.co.uk**
www.bridge-house.co.uk

f Bridge House Hotel, Beaminster
🐦 @the_bridgehouse

57

Riverside Restaurant

DORSET'S MUCH LOVED CLASSIC SEAFOOD RESTAURANT

For simply served, fresh and delicious seafood and a daily changing menu, it's hard to match the Riverside at West Bay. With a dining area on two levels and large picture windows, it's in a prime location, offering glorious river and countryside views. Family run, relaxed and friendly, this is a long established restaurant that's pioneered the use of fresh Dorset seafood to create the very best fish dishes, as well as alternative meat and vegetarian options. Pop in at lunchtime for the popular snack and sandwich menu. The Riverside was named one of the top four seafood restaurants in the South West in the *Good Food Guide 2014*.

Chef: **Tony Shaw**
3 course lunch from: **£27.50**
3 course dinner from: **£30**
Seats: **80**

West Bay, Bridport, Dorset, DT6 4EZ.
T: **01308 422011**
E: **info@thefishrestaurant-westbay.co.uk**
www.thefishrestaurant-westbay.co.uk

f Riverside Restaurant
🐦 @riversidewb

Highcliff Grill Restaurant

A TASTE OF DORSET ON THE CLIFFTOP

An iconic building high on the cliffs overlooking the sweeping sands of Bournemouth Beach is the home of one of Dorset's best restaurants. Many chefs are keen to use local produce in their menus, but Matt Budden, executive chef at the Highcliff Grill, must be one of the most dedicated. He's passionate about ingredients that come from the Dorset landscape – both sea and land – and is a true ambassador for the county's culinary bounty. Drawing on his extensive cheffing career, and always open to new ideas, he's created a vibrant and ever changing menu, with carefully crafted flavour combinations and some delightful surprises.

Chef: **Matt Budden**
3 course lunch from: **£20**
3 course dinner from: **£25**
Seats: **80**
Bedrooms: **160**
Room rate from: **£115**

Bournemouth Highcliff Marriott Hotel, St Michael's Road, Bournemouth, Dorset, BH2 5DU.

T: **01202 557702**
E: **mhrs.bohbm.fandb@marriotthotels.com**
www.highcliffgrill.co.uk

🅕 Highcliff Grill and Bar
🅣 @highcliffgrill

INSIDER'S TIP

'We have some of the best pubs and restaurants in the South West. My favourites include The Magdalen Chapter (p 81) in Exeter and Hix Oyster & Fish House (p 69) in Lyme Regis, for simple and classic dishes with lots of flavour.'

Alice Bowyer, Graze Bar, Brewery and Chophouse. p.51

DORSET & HAMPSHIRE

DORSET & HAMPSHIRE

59 ⑤

The Stapleton Arms

Enjoy comfort and style in equal portions at this former coaching inn. Great food is served in the elegant dining room which has a changing, seasonal menu, using produce brought in every day from the local markets. There's a spacious bar serving local ales, ciders and wines, along with draught and bottled beers from around the world. As a village pub, there's an air of laid-back simplicity combined with delicious decadence in the menu, and you can take a slice of Stapleton Arms magic with you: its famous scotch eggs and pork pies are available to go.

Chef: **Gabor Kiss**. 3 course lunch from: **£18**. 3 course dinner from: **£25**. Seats: **50**. Bedrooms: **4**. Room rate from: **£80**

Church Hill, Buckhorn Weston, Gillingham, Dorset, SP8 5HS.

T: 01963 370396
E: relax@thestapletonarms.com

www.thestapletonarms.com

The Stapleton Arms | Dorset Country Pub
@stapletonarms

60 ⑤

The Fontmell

It's not often that you find a babbling brook flowing between the bar and the dining room, but at The Fontmell, otter spotting is part of the dining experience. Chef-patron Tom Shaw carries the pub's distinctive character to the plate, introducing an eclectic mix of cuisines to the daily menu, where you'll find Indian mezzes alongside British classics. There are six luxurious bedrooms too, all named after butterflies, if you want to turn an indulgent meal into a foodie break.

Chef: **Tom Shaw**. 3 course lunch from: **£25**. 3 course dinner from: **£30**. Seats: **50**. Bedrooms: **6**. Room rate from: **£75**

Crown Hill, Fontmell Magna, Shaftesbury, Dorset, SP7 0PA.

T: 01747 811441
E: info@fontmell.com

info@thefontmell.com

The Fontmell
@thefontmell

61

The Acorn Inn

Set deep in the West Dorset countryside, the Acorn Inn sounds like it's come straight from a Thomas Hardy novel - which it has. The Grade I-listed 16th century coaching inn was mentioned in *Tess of the d'Ubervilles*. At the heart of the local community, it's also a popular haunt for foodies, with West Country produce taking pride of place in a thoughtful and varied menu. Fresh local fish and game feature alongside an excellent selection of ales, whiskies and wines. The downstairs area retains its original oak panelling, open fires and flagstone floors and the bespoke bedrooms have great character.

Chef: **Jack Mackenzie**. 3 course lunch from: **£23**. 3 course dinner from: **£23**. Seats: **60**. Bedrooms: **10**. Room rate from: **£99 (double)**

28 Fore Street, Evershot, Dorset, DT2 0JW.

T: 01935 83228
E: stay@acorn-inn.co.uk
www.acorn-inn.co.uk

The Acorn Inn
@acorn-inn

62

Hix Oyster and Fish House

Up high and overlooking the iconic harbour in Lyme Regis, this light and airy restaurant is one of Mark Hix's stable of seafood dining locations. Sit on the sunny terrace and enjoy the panoramic views across the Jurassic Coast while indulging in a great selection of British fish and seafood. The focus is on sourcing and serving the best produce that can be found and doing as little to it as possible - which of course means you get to sample the true flavours of the stunning foods the local landscape has to offer.

Chef: **Mark Hix**. 3 courses from: **£21 set menu or £27 à la carte**. Seats: **40/70**

Cobb Road, Lyme Regis, Dorset, DT7 3JP.

T: 01297 446910
E: reservations@hixoysterandfishhouse.co.uk
www.hixoysterandfishhouse.co.uk

HIX Restaurants
@hixlymeregis

63

Captains Club Hotel and Spa

Situated on the banks of the River Stour, just a short stroll from the historic market town of Christchurch, Captains Club is a great place for all-day dining, year round. The restaurant is styled in a modern take on a maritime theme, and the menu is fresh and innovative. During the summer months, alfresco dining is available, overlooking the bustle of boats and activity on the river, and the same view is enjoyed from each of the hotel's 29 bedrooms. Guests and non-guests alike can indulge in a treatment at the hotel's award winning spa or relax in the hydrotherapy pool and sauna.

Chef: **Andrew Gault**. 3 course lunch from: **£24**. 3 course dinner from: **£24**. Seats: **100**. Bedrooms: **1**. Room rate from: **£269**

Wick Ferry, Christchurch, Dorset, BH23 1HU.

T: 01202 475111
E: reservations@captainsclubhotel.com
www.captainsclubhotel.com

Captains Club Hotel and Spa
@theofficialcch

64

WestBeach

Just a few steps from Bournemouth's historic pier and practically sitting on the beach's golden sands, WestBeach is the ideal seaside restaurant. The menu is as lush as the surroundings with a focus on fresh seafood. It's caught locally by WestBeach's own fishing boats and prepared with other carefully selected local ingredients. With contemporary styling throughout, the restaurant features an open-plan kitchen so diners can watch the chefs at work, or simply relax and enjoy the stunning sea views – whatever the weather – through folding glass doors opening on to the decked terrace.

Chef: **Marcin Pacholarz**. 3 course lunch from: **£24**. 3 course dinner from: **£24**. Seats: **80**

Pier Approach, Bournemouth, Dorset, BH2 5AA.

T: 01202 587785
E: enquiry@west-beach.co.uk
www.west-beach.co.uk

WestBeach
@westbeachbmouth

DORSET & HAMPSHIRE

Taste the
Original Fruit
without having to
Concentrate

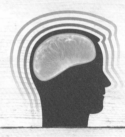

You could say that most fruit juices leave a little too much to the imagination.
Vacuumed and vapourised with aromas added in later, they are quite removed from the
original fruit flavour. Frobishers fruit juices, fruit smoothies and juice drinks are made from
perfectly ripe fruit that is simply squeezed, pressed and bottled.
No concentrates. Nothing artificial. Just fruit juice that's
as deliciously true to its origins as possible.

65

Arbor Restaurant

Passion, inspiration and the thrill of discovering something that little bit different – Arbor's chef Andy Hilton knows how to create an original dining experience. The restaurant is in The Green House, a stylish eco-hotel and Grade II Victorian villa in the heart of Bournemouth. With its own beehives on the roof, it's no surprise there's a commitment to sustainably sourced and seasonal ingredients. Andy, who trained with Gordon Jones in Bath, uses a treasured collection of artisan suppliers to create his two AA rosette dishes.

Chef: **Andy Hilton**. 3 course lunch from: **£20**. 3 course dinner from: **£28**. Seats: **38**. Bedrooms: **32**. Room rate from: **£99**

The Green House, 4 Grove Road, Bournemouth, Dorset, BH1 3AX.

T: **01202 498900**
E: **reservations@thegreenhousehotel.com**

www.arbor-restaurant.co.uk

Arbor Restaurant - Relaxed Dining Bournemouth
@arborrest

66

Crab House Cafe

Chef-proprietor Nigel Bloxham has set his parents the task of growing the herbs used in his restaurant, and there's a veg patch right alongside the wooden shack which overlooks Chesil Beach and the Portland coast. What lies behind the unassuming exterior draws diners from near and far, and seafood is the star. It comes from Weymouth, Brixham and Poole and the menu depends entirely on what's landed – often changing twice a day. The Crab House also has its own oyster farm, and you'll often meet farmer David hauling in oysters, ready to be eaten within minutes.

Chef: **Nigel Bloxham**. 3 course lunch from: **£25**. 3 course dinner from: **25**. Seats: **48**

Ferrymans Way, Portland Road, Wyke Regis, Weymouth, Dorset, DT4 9YU.

T: **01305 788867**
E: **bookings@crabhousecafe.co.uk**

www.crabhousecafe.co.uk

Crab House Cafe
@crabhousecafe

TRENCHERMAN'S ONLINE

On the web

Find the full list of restaurants, read the latest features and book online at many of the restaurants in the guide on the website:
www.trenchermans-guide.com

On your tablet

Download the guide from **iTunes**, **Google Play** and **www.pocketmags.com**

Twitter and Facebook

Join the conversation on
Twitter: **@trenchermans**
Facebook: **The Trencherman's Guide**

DEVON

Devon's abundant with exceptional gourmet
experiences - from two-Michelin starred cooking
to chilled pub dining.

Devon

67 Watersmeet Hotel
68 The Coach House by Michael Caines
69 Saunton Sands Hotel
70 The Masons Arms
71 The Swan
72 Combe House Devon
73 The Salty Monk
74 The Riviera Hotel and Restaurant
75 La Petite Maison
76 Les Saveurs at The Seafood Restaurant
77 The Magdalen Chapter

78 ABode Exeter
79 Cary Arms
80 Waterside Bistro
81 Gidleigh Park
82 Prince Hall Hotel and Restaurant
83 The Two Bridges Hotel
84 Soar Mill Cove Hotel
85 The Dartmoor Inn
86 Lewtrenchard Manor
87 The Treby Arms
88 The Arundell Arms Hotel and Restaurant
89 The Horn of Plenty

90 Rock Salt Cafe Brasserie
91 Yeoldon House Hotel
92 Northcote Manor Country House Hotel
93 The Hartnoll Hotel
94 The Lazy Toad Inn
95 The Rusty Bike
96 The Salutation Inn
97 The Galley Restaurant
98 Rodean Restaurant
99 The Orange Tree Restaurant
100 The Horse
101 Ilsington Country House Hotel
102 The Royal Seven Stars Hotel
103 The Grill Room
104 The Riverford Field Kitchen
105 Plantation House
106 Barbican Kitchen
107 Langdon Court Restaurant
108 Rhodes @ the Dome
109 The Cornish Arms
110 Hotel Endsleigh

Barnstaple
Okehampton
Cullompton
Exeter
Topsham
Sidmouth
Plymouth
Dartmouth
Salcombe

New in the guide this year:

The Dartmoor Inn, Les Saveurs at the Seafood Restaurant, Saunton Sands Hotel, Ilsington County House Hotel, Yeoldon House Hotel, Northcote Manor Country House Hotel, Plantation House Hotel and Restaurant, The Royal Seven Stars Hotel and Rhodes @ The Dome.

Restaurants listed in the guide correspond to the numbers plotted on the map. Locations are approximate.

67 💲
Watersmeet Hotel

CHIC BEACHSIDE DINING AT WOOLACOMBE

Escape to another world at this chic coastal hotel overlooking Woolacombe, often ranked one of the best beaches in Britain. Period the property may be, but inside you'll find chic bedrooms, an indoor pool and spa and classical English cooking with European influences. Wherever you dine you'll enjoy that stunning beachy backdrop, so choose between the contemporary restaurant, the chilled out bistro, or kick back on the terrace and indulge in cocktails or a cream tea.

Chef: **John Prince**
3 course lunch from: **£25**
3 course dinner from: **£42**
Seats: **60**
Bedrooms: **29**
Room rate from: **£90**

Woolacombe, Devon, EX34 7EB.
T: **01271 870333**
E: **info@watersmeethotel.co.uk**
www.watersmeethotel.co.uk

f Watersmeet Hotel
🐦 @watersmeethotel

68 💲
The Coach House by Michael Caines

TOP NOTCH DINING ON THE EDGE OF EXMOOR

North Devon's most exciting new restaurant, The Coach House by Michael Caines, sees the two Michelin-starred chef bringing his signature flair – and dishes – to this attractive restaurant housed in a converted 17th century coaching house.

With Caines protégé, head chef Thomas Hine at the helm, the team is creating fabulous dining which has already earned them two AA rosettes. Strong links to local producers (crab from Lundy and chicken from the farm down the road), an attractive bar and armchair-filled loft space for cocktails and coffee, plus sumptuous bedrooms in the hotel building, make this a must-visit destination.

Chef: **Thomas Hine**
3 course lunch from: **£19.95**
3 course dinner from: **£38**
Seats: **50**
Bedrooms: **16**
Room rate from: **£125**

Kentisbury, Barnstaple, Devon, EX31 4NL.
T: **01271 882295**
E: **coachhouse@kentisburygrange.com**
www.kentisburygrange.com

f Kentisbury Grange
🐦 @kgcoachhouse

DEVON

69 💲
Saunton Sands Hotel

ART DECO GLAMOUR BY THE SEA

This lovely art deco hotel overlooks one of the UK's most stunning beaches, Saunton Sands. Guests can visit for AA rosette quality lunch or dinner, and a beautiful traditional afternoon tea served in the refurbished deco Terrace Lounge, but to appreciate the full experience a stay is in order. There's a warm, friendly, all-generations atmosphere at this family run hotel which sees guests returning year after year, and constant redecoration of the rooms makes it a smart spot for a grown up gourmet getaway – or a foodie retreat with the family.

Chef: **Boyd Snelling**
3 course lunch from: **£22.50**
3 course dinner from: **£36**
Seats: **150**
Bedrooms: **83**
Room rate from: **£90**

70 ▢
The Masons Arms

MICHELIN-STARRED DELIGHTS IN A RURAL IDYLL ON EXMOOR

Down the lanes, deep in the north Devon countryside, it's a delight to discover this Michelin-starred restaurant. A decade ago, after 12 years as head chef at Michel Roux's Waterside Inn in Bray, Mark Dodson and his wife Sarah moved to this 13th century thatched inn. Their Michelin star followed in 2006, and has been retained ever since. The food, a modern take on British and French classics, is complex, precise and highly assured. Dine in the bright dining room with a painted mural ceiling and views of rolling hills. Alongside the sophisticated menus, the Masons still retains its local pub feel with log fires, wooden beams and a warm welcome.

Chef: **Mark Dodson**
3 course lunch from: **£25**
3 course dinner from: **£40**
Seats: **28**

Saunton, near Braunton, Devon, EX33 1LQ.
T: 01271 890212
E: reservations@sauntonsands.com
www.sauntonsands.co.uk

Saunton Sands Hotel
@sauntonsandshot

Knowstone, South Molton, Devon, EX36 4RY.
T: 01398 341231
E: enqs@masonsarmsdevon.co.uk
www.masonsarmsdevon.co.uk

The Masons Arms Knowstone
@masonsknowstone

DEVON

71 ◈ ▢

The Swan

EVERYONE'S FAVOURITE LOCAL

This lovely traditional pub in the village of Bampton, near Exmoor National Park, dates back to the 15th century and still has the original fireplace and bread oven to warm guests through winter. Famed for its Sunday lunches, The Swan's menus showcase British pub classics made with produce sourced from the rural Devon surroundings, as well as dishes in a fine dining style. Owners Paul and Donna Berry serve up accomplished, honest food, in hearty portions, complemented by a decent selection of local ales and good wines by the glass. With its community spirit and jolly atmosphere, The Swan is the ideal local pub we all wish we had on our doorstep.

Chef: **Paul Berry**
3 course lunch from: **£20**
3 course dinner from: **£25**
Seats: **60**
Bedrooms: **3**
Room rate from: **£90**

Station Road, Briton Street, Bampton, Devon, EX16 9NG.

T: **01398 332248**
E: **info@theswan.co**

www.theswan.co

[f] The Swan
[t] @theswanbampton

72 ◈

Combe House Devon

ROMANTIC HOTEL WITH AWARD WINNING RESTAURANT

Grabbing the Best Restaurant accolade in the 2015 *Food* Reader Awards, Combe House is flying high. Set in 3,500 acres, this breathtakingly beautiful Elizabethan manor house exudes history and elegant luxury, while retaining plenty of individual, quirky touches. Heading up the kitchen team is Hadleigh Barrett with sous chef Stuart Brown, both Master Chefs of Great Britain. The chaps make good use of the manor's kitchen garden which has been gradually restored over the years, and guests are free to wander the grounds and explore too. If the chefs are passionate about producing exquisite dishes, then the same level of dedication goes into the wines, which are housed in Combe's ancient cellars. This is a very special place indeed.

Chef: **Hadleigh Barrett**
2 course lunch from: **£29, with lighter meals available during the day**
3 course dinner from: **£54**
Seats: **75 (in three dining rooms)**
Bedrooms: **15, plus 2 thatched cottages for 2-8 guests**
Room rate from: **£220**

Gittisham, Honiton, Devon, EX14 3AD.

T: **01404 540400**
E: **stay@combehousedevon.com**

www.combehousedevon.com

[f] Combe House Hotel Devon
[t] @combehousedevon

73 ⑤
The Salty Monk

ACCOMPLISHED COOKING NEAR SIDMOUTH

Expect highly accomplished food and a warm welcome at this family run restaurant just outside of Sidmouth. The setting is modern and comfortable and there's a pleasing contrast between the fine dining Garden Room Restaurant and the more relaxed Abbots Den Brasserie. Common to both are robust flavours and seasonal dishes created with a contemporary twist. A great amount of care goes into finding local, ethically produced ingredients and this attention to detail continues with the cooking and presentation. Indulge in a leisurely evening meal or Sunday lunch, or visit the brasserie for tasting platters, snacks and specials.

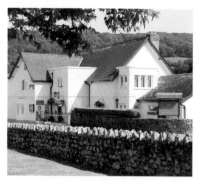

Chef: **Andy Witheridge**
3 course lunch from: £24
3 course dinner from: £30
Seats: 36
Bedrooms: 6
Room rate from: £130

Church Street, Sidford, Sidmouth, Devon, EX10 9QP.

T: **01395 513174**
E: **saltymonk@btconnect.com**
www.saltymonk.co.uk

f The Salty Monk Restaurant With Rooms
🐦 @saltymonk

74 ⑤
The Riviera Hotel and Restaurant

ELEGANT DINING BY THE SEA IN SMART SIDMOUTH

For refined dining in a glamorous seaside hotel, head to this elegant two AA rosette restaurant. Extensive menus use the best fresh and locally sourced produce, with seafood a speciality – fish, crab and lobster all come from a third-generation local family fishing business. Extend the dining experience with a pre dinner or late night cocktail in the Regency Bar and the rather indulgent traditional afternoon tea is another must. Pop in for a light lunch and during the warmer months you can dine alfresco, soaking up the chic ambience on the sunny terrace. Of course you'll discover an impeccable attention to detail and the warm welcome you'd expect in a private hotel of this quality.

Chef: **Martin Osedo**
2 course lunch: **£25**, 4 course lunch: **£29.50**
3 course dinner from: **£38**
Seats: **80 in restaurant, 60 on terrace**
Bedrooms: **26**

The Esplanade, Sidmouth, Devon, EX10 8AY.

T: **01395 515201**
E: **enquiries@hotelriviera.co.uk**
www.hotelriviera.co.uk

75

La Petite Maison

PERFECTLY EXECUTED FOOD IN A CHIC SEA TOWN

Husband and wife team Douglas and Elizabeth Pestell have created a charming restaurant in the centre of historic Topsham where they've now reached their 15th year of consistently delighting diners. It's easy to see why: white tablecloths, comfy elegant chairs, and a view through the restaurant's bow windows into the narrow street make this a hugely appealing place to spend an evening. The warm and friendly welcome is matched by the confident dishes coming out of the kitchen. Classically trained chef Douglas has built good links with his local suppliers and he uses this West Country produce to create a modern and well executed menu.

Chef: **Douglas Pestell**
3 course lunch from: **£38.95**
3 course dinner from: **£38.95**
Seats: **28**

35 Fore Street, Topsham, Exeter, Devon, EX3 0HR.

T: **01392 873660**
E: **dougandliz@lapetitemaison.co.uk**
www.lapetitemaison.co.uk

 @chefdouglpm

76

Les Saveurs at the Seafood Restaurant

SUBLIME SEAFOOD WITH OODLES OF GALLIC PERSONALITY

If he's not in the kitchen, chances are you'll find chef Olivier Guyard-Mulkerrin in the sea off the Exmouth coast, spearfishing for the star of his latest culinary creation. This chef is not just passionate about cooking, he lives and breathes it. Shunning fads and fashions, Olivier draws on his family background, heritage and on his ability to turn the sea's produce into sublime dishes. Linger a while over a coffee and you may hear tales of those underwater adventures. This simply styled, neighbourhood restaurant has been quietly building attention and is now, deservedly, notching up the awards.

Chef: **Olivier Guyard-Mulkerrin**
3 course dinner from: **£33**
Seats: **54**

9 Tower Street, Exmouth, Devon, EX8 1NT.

T: **01395 269459**
E: **lessaveurs@yahoo.co.uk**
www.lessaveurs.co.uk

Les Saveurs
@les_saveurs

forest produce

SPECIALIST INGREDIENTS FOR CHEFS

77 💲

The Magdalen Chapter

COOL DINING IN THE CENTRE OF EXETER

Set in a 19th century eye hospital, this sleek hotel not only has an intriguing past, but also captivating décor to match. With a maze of intricate corridors that lead to a stylish cocktail bar and cosy areas to hang out in – it even has its own library – The Magdalen Chapter is more of a destination than just a place to stay. The contemporary styling carries through to the food, with chef Matt Downing taking centre stage in the theatre kitchen, where he turns classic ingredients into simple, seasonal and masterfully created dishes. Look out for special themed dining evenings and cookery masterclasses throughout the year.

Chef: **Matt Downing**
3 course lunch from: **£16.95**
3 course dinner from: **£16.95**
Seats: **75**
Bedrooms: **59**
Room rate from: **£150**

Magdalen Street, Exeter, Devon, EX2 4HY.
T: **01392 281000**
E: **magdalen_ge@chapterhotels.com**
www.themagdalenchapter.com

📘 The Magdalen Chapter
🐦 @magdalenchpt

78 💲

ABode Exeter

DINE IN STYLE WITH CATHEDRAL VIEWS

The building that houses ABode Exeter stands proudly as it has done for the past 300 years on Exeter's beautiful Cathedral Green at the heart of the city. Originally a 17th century coaching inn – said to be Britain's oldest hotel – ABode Exeter is a rather more glamorous affair nowadays, with modern, luxury accommodation alongside outstanding culinary credentials. Executive chef Nick Topham has created menus that offer simple yet sublime modern British cuisine, using nothing but the finest produce and seasonal ingredients, locally sourced from Devon and the South West. A great base from which to explore the historic city.

Chef: **Nick Topham**
3 course lunch from: **£19.95**
3 course dinner from: **£22.95**
Seats: **60**
Bedrooms: **53**
Room rate from: **£89**

Cathedral Yard, Exeter, Devon, EX1 1HD.
T: **01392 319955**
E: **info@abodeexeter.co.uk**
www.abodeexeter.co.uk

📘 ABode Hotels
🐦 @abodeexeter

DEVON

79 💲
Cary Arms

GASTRO DINING ON THE COAST

Fondly known as The Inn on the Beach, this gem on the south Devon coast has all the comforts of a family inn with the style and amenities of a boutique hotel. With a large menu showcasing quality pub dining at its best, there are hearty classics such as roasted loin of venison, River Exe mussels and sausages with mash to dig into; and it's a perfect spot for long lunches and lazy suppers. In winter, the bar's the place to cosy up by the roaring fire with a local ale. In summer, enjoy lunch alfresco on the terrace, with unrivalled views across the bay. With a number of stylish rooms and a couple of quaint cottages, there's plenty of room at the inn if you want to linger a little longer.

Chef: **Ben Kingdon**
3 course lunch from: **£21**
3 course dinner from: **£21**
Seats: **65**
Bedrooms: **8, and 4 cottages**
Room rate from: **£195**

80
Waterside Bistro

POPULAR SEAFOOD BISTRO BY THE BEAUTIFUL RIVER DART

Chef Matt Buzzo has given his popular riverside bistro a subtle makeover for 2015. Alongside the superb menu featuring seafood specialities, new chilled cabinet displays offer tempting sweet treats such as frangipane tarts and bramley apple cake alongside house favourites like scones, carrot cake and lemon polenta cake. Run by Matt and his wife Delphine, the bistro is a favourite place to eat by the beautiful River Dart, especially with its outdoor terrace and canopied area. Open seven days a week from 9am for breakfast to chilled out evening dining.

Chef: **Matt Buzzo**
3 course lunch from: **£22**
3 course dinner from: **£25**
Seats: **62 inside, 160 outside (80 covered)**

Babbacombe Beach, Babbacombe, Devon, TQ1 3LX.
T: **01803 327110**
E: **enquiries@caryarms.co.uk**
www.caryarms.co.uk

🅵 The Cary Arms
🐦 @caryarms

The Plains, Totnes, Devon, TQ9 5YS.
T: **01803 864069**
E: **restaurant@watersidebistro.com**
www.watersidebistro.com

🅵 Waterside Bistro Totnes
🐦 @totneswaterside

DEVON

81 ⑤
Gidleigh Park

TWO MICHELIN-STARRED DINING ON DARTMOOR

Set majestically on the upper reaches of the River Teign, Gidleigh Park enjoys an exquisite location on the edge of Dartmoor National Park. Famed for its culinary credentials, Gidleigh Park offers an air of tranquillity and romance within a Tudor-style country house, beautifully furnished and surrounded by 107 acres of mature grounds. Critically acclaimed two Michelin-starred executive chef Michael Caines MBE and his team create dishes using seasonal, locally sourced ingredients from the West Country – including from Gidleigh Park's own kitchen garden. The restaurant is also renowned for its extensive wine list, with around 13,000 bottles stored in the cellar.

DEVON

Chef: **Michael Caines MBE**. 3 course lunch from: **£58.50**. 3 course dinner from: **£118**. Seats: **50**. Bedrooms: **24**. Room rate from: **£280**

Chagford, Devon, TQ13 8HH.
T: **01647 432367**
E: info@gidleigh.co.uk
www.gidleigh.co.uk

f Gidleigh Park
🐦 @gidleighhotel

Being a Michelin three Star restaurant for more than two decades creates a responsibility which is now part of our daily life.

We feel - and most importantly our customers too - that THE WATERSIDE INN and HILDON are a perfect marriage.

Alain Roux

HILDON
NATURAL MINERAL WATER

www.hildon.com

82 $

Prince Hall Hotel and Restaurant

WALKERS' PARADISE ON THE MOOR

This foodie escape in the heart of beautiful Dartmoor is a real find. Authentic and welcoming, with an emphasis on good cooking, the team here creates a destination dine-and-stay experience that welcomes four legged-friends with as much warmth as their owners. And with the rugged moor just a step away from the dining room, it's a walkers' paradise. Food in the restaurant, including meats, cheeses and beers, is sourced from the surrounding area – with vegetables and salad leaves coming from the hotel's kitchen garden. Even the table water comes from the moor. Pop in for morning coffee, fabulous cream teas, lunch or fine dining in the evening.

3 course lunch from: **£24.95**
3 course dinner from: **£47.50**
Seats: **20**
Bedrooms:**8**
Room rate from: **£190**

Two Bridges, Yelverton, Devon, PL20 6SA.
T: **01822 890403**
E: **info@princehall.co.uk**
www.princehall.co.uk

Prince Hall Hotel & Restaurant
@Princehallhotel

83 $

The Two Bridges Hotel

WILDLY ROMANTIC RETREAT ON DARTMOOR

A delightful hotel filled with charm and nostalgia, The Two Bridges is an oasis of comfort in the heart of Dartmoor. Cosy lounges with log fires in winter and summer alfresco tables with sweeping lawns fringed by the River Dart make for an idyllic setting. Enjoy fabulous dining using local Dartmoor and regional produce that reflect the light touch of elegance and flavours that have earned executive chef Mike Palmer and his team accolades across the South West.

Chef: **Mike Palmer**
3 course lunch from: **£21.95**
3 course dinner from: **£37.50**
Seats: **60**
Bedrooms:**32**
Room rate from: **£150**

Two Bridges, Devon, PL20 6SW.
T: **01822 892300**
E: **reception@twobridges.co.uk**
www.twobridges.co.uk

Two Bridges Hotel
@two_bridges

TRENCHERMAN'S
AWARDS

**BEST FRONT OF
HOUSE TEAM
2015**

Soar Mill Cove Hotel

LUXURIOUS, FAMILY RUN RETREAT BY THE COAST

Just off the South West Coast Path, hidden away in its own secluded valley, Soar Mill Cove is a luxurious modern hotel. The surrounding stunning scenery provides an inspiring backdrop to a meal in its excellent restaurant. Contemporary styling is complemented by traditional family-friendly hotel values and a warm welcome. Knowing that good food makes a holiday, fresh produce and quality cooking is the order of the day, with local ingredients such as hand-picked Salcombe crab, Start Bay scallops, Gressingham duckling and homegrown herbs. Three generations of the Makepeace family take great care to make this delightful Devon beach hotel a great destination.

DEVON

Chef: **Ian Macdonald**. 3 course set lunch: **£23**. 3 course dinner from: **£35**. Seats: **60**. Bedrooms:**22**. Room rate from: **£159**

Malborough, near Salcombe, Devon, TQ7 3DS.

T: 01548 561566
E: info@soarmillcove.co.uk
www.soarmillcove.co.uk

f Soar Mill Cove Hotel
🐦 @soarmillcove

85 ⑤

The Dartmoor Inn

CLASSIC FOOD IN A CHIC MOORLAND PUB

Within walking distance of the moor, this cosy old pub provides a welcome dose of good food in a relaxing and atmospheric setting. Proprietor Philip Burgess and co-chef Andrew Honey have gained a loyal following with their well thought out menus, and a refurbishment has brought out the character of the stylish bedrooms. Authentic, expertly cooked food uses the best locally sourced ingredients such as Devon ruby red beef and fish from Looe market. The restaurant consists of a series of smaller dining rooms, so you can enjoy an intimate dining experience here or eat in the bar with its open log fire. Go for smart food and fine wines or local ales and pub classics such as fish and chips, steak sandwiches and the slow roast beef brisket on Sundays.

Chefs: **Andrew Honey and Philip Burgess**
3 course lunch from: **£15**
3 course dinner from: **£20**
Seats: **65**
Bedrooms: **4**
Room rate from: **£95**

Moorside, Lydford, Okehampton, Devon, EX20 4AY.
T: **01822 820221**
E: **info@dartmoorinn.co.uk**
www.dartmoorinn.com

🐦 @thedartmoorinn

86 ⑤

Lewtrenchard Manor

HOMEGROWN DELIGHTS AT THE MANOR

The stuff of storybooks, this beautiful family owned Jacobean manor house, tucked away in a valley on the edge of Dartmoor, is a magical setting for head chef Matthew Peryer's exquisite dishes. He uses seasonal ingredients, including produce from the hotel's walled garden, to create a menu of balanced, delightful dishes. Watch him and his team at work by dining at the Purple Carrot chef's table – with screens showing all the action taking place in the kitchen – or eat in the wood panelled dining room, before retiring to a sofa in front of the fabulous carved fireplace. In the summer, head for the Italianate courtyard, with its blue haze of 100-year-old wisterias for lunch or pre-dinner drinks.

Chef: **Matthew Peryer**
3 course lunch from: **£24**
3 course dinner from: **£49.50**
Seats: **40**
Bedrooms: **14**
Room rate from: **£165**

Lewdown, Okehampton, Devon, EX20 4PN.
T: **01566 783222**
E: **info@lewtrenchard.co.uk**
www.lewtrenchard.co.uk

f Lewtrenchard Manor
🐦 @lewtrenchard

From ship to plate in 48 hours

Proud to support The Trencherman's Guide
and all our customers

flying fish
·SEAFOODS·

01726 862876 | www.flyingfishseafoods.co.uk

87
The Treby Arms

INNOVATIVE COOKING FROM
A MULTI-AWARD WINNING CHEF

A pub reputedly built by the famous engineer Isambard Kingdom Brunel is the home of another celebrity, in the form of Michelin star-holding chef Anton Piotrowski. In addition to previously winning *Masterchef: The Professionals*, this year he also won the first ever Trencherman's Best Restaurant award. The chef has been doing his own bit of transformative building work since he and his wife Clare took over the 18th century village pub four years ago, and extra seating upstairs and an enlarged bar area have enhanced the pub's appeal as a friendly local. The food continues to be exceptional, with constantly changing menus that are timed perfectly with the seasons and showcased at their best in the beautiful tasting menu.

Chef: **Anton Piotrowski**. 3 course lunch from: **£20**. 3 course dinner from: **£40**. Seats: **60**

6 Newtons Row, Sparkwell, Devon, PL7 5DD.
T: **01752 837363**
E: **trebyarms@hotmail.co.uk**
www.thetrebyarms.co.uk

f Treby Arms
🐦 @thetrebyarms

The Arundell Arms Hotel and Restaurant

A TASTE OF THE COUNTRY ON THE DEVON AND CORNWALL BORDER

Fishing lodge, country pub and fine dining restaurant – The Arundell Arms is many things to many people. There's a strong country sports theme running through the establishment, which translates into the use of local game in season on the menu. Master Chef Steven Pidgeon is at the helm in the kitchen, and there's great customer care and front of house service as a result of the hotel being owned by the same family for more than 50 years. Set in a valley with five rivers, close to the uplands of Dartmoor, The Arundell Arms is a fantastic and authentic base from which to explore the surrounding countryside. Guests can also enjoy the top class fly fishing school on offer.

Chef: **Steve Pidgeon**
3 course lunch from: **£23**
3 course dinner from: **£47.50**
Seats: **80**
Bedrooms: **26**
Room rate from: **£180**

Fore Street, Lifton, Devon, PL16 0AA.
T: **01566 784666**
E: **reservations@arundellarms.com**
www.arundellarms.com

f The Arundell Arms Hotel
𝕏 @thearundellarms

The Horn of Plenty

ROOMS WITH A VIEW AT THIS FOODIE HOTEL

This boutique country house hotel has long been associated with excellent food and current head chef Scott Paton keeps the tradition alive and well. Scott produces dishes which are immaculate in flavour and presentation, using ingredients of which 90 per cent come from the South West. Leave room for one of his famed desserts and savour the culinary experience while gazing out over the Tamar Valley panorama. The house was built for a 19th century mine captain, who clearly appreciated its elevated position. The elegant past is reflected in all aspects of the house and restaurant, but with Scott's confident, modern cooking and the 16 chic bedrooms, The Horn of Plenty is also a luxurious place to stay. Last year saw the opening of six new Coach House rooms, each beautifully designed and furnished with most boasting balconies with stunning views over the Tamar Valley.

Chef: **Scott Paton**
3 course lunch from: **£24.50**
3 course dinner from: **£49.50**
Seats: **60**
Bedrooms: **16**
Room rate from: **£95**

Gulworthy, Tavistock, Devon, PL19 8JD.
T: **01822 832528**
E: **enquiries@thehornofplenty.co.uk**
www.thehornofplenty.co.uk

f The Horn of Plenty Country House and Restaurant
𝕏 @hornofplenty1

DEVON

Rock Salt
Cafe Brasserie

PLYMOUTH'S HIDDEN GEM

Rock Salt's chef Dave Jenkins is driven by a passion for good, honest food, and the result is a host of ardent fans, who have embraced this unassuming little restaurant that's become a foodie hub in Plymouth. Situated quite close to the city's ferry port, this is one for the title of hidden gem. Rock Salt draws diners from far and wide to the up-and-coming Millbay area for Dave's imaginative cooking. Visit for all-day breakfasts, light lunches and brasserie style evening menus which reveal a fine dining heritage on the part of the chef. There's also an unexpected dash of Asian influence – and a warm welcome, of course.

INSIDER'S TIP

'The Treby Arms (p 89) is at the top of my list to visit, I've heard great things about it.'

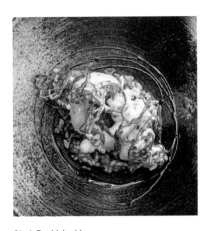

Chef: **David Jenkins**
3 course lunch from: **£18**
3 course dinner from: **£22**
Seats: **70**

31 Stonehouse Street, Plymouth, Devon, PL1 3PE.

T: **01752 225522**
E: **info@rocksaltcafe.co.uk**
www.rocksaltcafe.co.uk

f Rock Salt Cafe Brasserie
🐦 @rocksaltcafeuk

DEVON

**Gordon Jones,
Menu Gordon Jones.** p.47

DEVON

91 $

Yeoldon House Hotel

Under new ownership and opening its restaurant doors to non-residents for the first time, Yeoldon House Hotel is a relative newcomer to the Devon dining scene. Formerly of The Masons Arms, chef Daniel Tugwell heads up the kitchen, where local and seasonal produce are brought together in sophisticated dishes. With picturesque views over beautiful gardens and the river beyond, the elegant restaurant provides a refined setting for an intimate meal and there are ten bedrooms if you'd like to lengthen your visit.

Chef: **Daniel Tugwell**. 3 course dinner from: **£40**. Seats: **26**. Bedrooms: **10**. Room rate from: **£125**

Durrant Lane, Northam, Bideford, Devon, EX39 2RL.

T: 01237 474400
E: info@yeoldonhouse.co.uk

www.yeoldonhouse.co.uk

f Yeoldon House Hotel and Restaurant
𝕏 @yeoldondining

92 $

Northcote Manor Country House Hotel

This beautiful 18th-century manor is hidden at the end of a wooded drive in north Devon's Taw Valley. It's blissfully peaceful, with the restaurant overlooking 20 acres of sweeping lawns and ancient woodland. The atmosphere is relaxed and quietly sophisticated, upheld by an attentive yet discreet service team. The hotel's 16 rooms have each been carefully styled and the menu at the two AA rosette restaurant is similarly kept up-to-date, refreshed to match the season every couple of months.

Chef: **Richie Herkes**. 3 course lunch from: **£25.50**. 3 course dinner from: **£45**. Seats: **32**. Bedrooms: **16**. Room rate from: **£170**

Burrington, near Umberleigh, Devon, EX37 9LZ.

T: 01769 560501
E: rest@northcotemanor.co.uk

www.northcotemanor.co.uk

f Northcote Manor
𝕏 @northcotedevon

93

The Hartnoll Hotel

On the edge of Exmoor National Park, and surrounded by rolling green hills, this boutique hotel showcases its location in its menu. Local fish and game make regular appearances alongside Devon cider, Devonshire blue cheese and its own Hartnoll chutney. A favourite with the shooting set, the Hartnoll is rooted in the Exmoor tradition, and offers yet more tradition in its easy access to National Trust property, Knightshayes, across the road. Discover a variety of menus, from afternoon tea to an à la carte dinner menu, and dig into a handpicked wine list to match.

Chef: **Steve Cox**. 3 course lunch from: **£23**. 3 course dinner from: **£30**. Seats: **Up to 100**. Bedrooms: **18**. Room rate from: **£100**

Bolham, Tiverton, Devon, EX16 7RA.

T: 01884 252777
E: frontdesk@hartnollhotel.co.uk

www.hartnollhotel.co.uk

Hartnoll Hotel
@hartnollhotel

94

The Lazy Toad Inn

The Lazy Toad is a Grade II-listed inn situated in the picturesque village of Brampford Speke. The emphasis is on locally sourced food, with new chef Craig Beacham (formerly of The Elephant in Torquay) using high quality, sustainable produce to create a simple but tantalising menu. Accompany your meal with a selection from a list of real ales, ciders and wines. There are five ensuite rooms with oak beamed ceilings and a gorgeous pub garden with cobbled courtyard. In winter, we'd recommend grabbing a seat in front of the log fire. Well behaved dogs on a lead are welcome.

Chef: **Craig Beacham**. 3 course lunch from: **£22.95**. 3 course dinner from: **£22.95**. Seats: **65**. Bedrooms: **5**. Room rate from: **£85**

Brampford Speke, Exeter, Devon, EX5 5DP.

T: 01392 841591
E: thelazytoadinn@outlook.com

www.thelazytoadinn.com

The Lazy Toad Inn
@thelazytoadinn

95

The Rusty Bike

As well as showcasing the culinary talents of chef Darren Jory, the Rusty pays homage to the backstreet boozer. Owner Hamish Lothian took it on six years ago after long wanting to create the perfect pub. And he's certainly done it. The rusty revels in real ales (including from its own Fat Pig brewery), spirits from across the globe and an extensive wine list. It's also filled with characters, including its own resident gamekeeper, and of course chef Darren, who grows his own veg and is known to scoot off on fishing trips with Hamish. This is a pub that's become a character in its own right.

Chef: **Darren Jory**. Lunch (Sunday only): **£10**. 3 course dinner from: **£30**. Seats: **100**

67 Howell Road, Exeter, Devon, EX4 4LZ.

T: 01392 214440
E: tiny@therustybike-exeter.co.uk

www.rustybike-exeter.co.uk

The Rusty Bike
@rustybikeexeter

96

The Salutation Inn

Set in a beautiful 18th century building in the historic port town of Topsham, The Salutation Inn is steeped in historic charm. The renovated inn perfectly balances the building's original features with contemporary design, with six bedrooms available for weary travellers. Lunch is enjoyed in the striking glass atrium, where head chef Tom Williams-Hawkes sources the seafood and fish from the River Exe. The real star of the show here is the evening taster menu, which changes weekly. Expect to encounter adventurous dishes with a modern, French influence.

Chef: **Tom Williams-Hawkes**. Lunch from: **£8.50**. Tasting menus from: **£39.50**. Seats: **26**. Bedrooms: **6**. Room rate from: **£135**

68 Fore Street, Topsham, Devon, EX3 0HL.

T: 01392 873060
E: info@salutationtopsham.co.uk

www.salutationtopsham.co.uk

Salutation Inn
@salutation1

97

The Galley Restaurant

This bijou restaurant in Topsham near Exeter is a find for beautiful cooking presented with care and attention to detail. Chef Dolton Lodge, a former finalist in the Master Chefs of Great Britain Young Chef of the Year competition, creates the restaurant's speciality seafood dishes, with Asian influences such as lime and ginger Brixham crab, and soy, garlic and ginger stir-fried king prawns, alongside classic British and French cooking. Quality local meats are also on the menu, and the service is intimate and thoughtful.

Chef: **Dolton Lodge**. 2 course set lunch from: **£17**. 3 course dinner from: **£32.50**. Seats: **48**

41 Fore Street, Topsham, Exeter, Devon, EX3 0HU.

T: 01392 876078
E: fish@galleyrestaurant.co.uk
www.galleyrestaurant.co.uk

The Galley Restaurant Topsham
@galleytopsham

98

Rodean Restaurant

Accomplished chef Matthew Tilt and his wife Elizabeth are the creators of Rodean Restaurant in Kenton and have built a strong following of regular customers through word of mouth. Beams and dark wood panelling make an atmospheric setting for a relaxed and personal dining experience. Exciting and varied, menus combining the best of British with international influences are lovingly prepared using some of the West Country's finest produce.

Chef: **Matthew Tilt**. Lunch (Sunday only): **£21**. 3 course dinner from: **£21**. Seats: **38**

The Triangle, Kenton, Exeter, Devon, EX6 8LS.

T: 01626 890195
E: rodeanrestaurant@gmail.com
www.rodeanrestaurant.co.uk

Rodean Restaurant
@rodean_kenton

99

The Orange Tree Restaurant

Staying true to their classical culinary roots, husband and wife team Sharon and Bernd Wolf have created a popular neighbourhood restaurant, just a few steps from the harbour in Torquay. The à la carte, seasonal menu is English/European in style and enhanced by chef Bernd's individual flair. Food is served in a relaxed, unhurried atmosphere with pride clearly taken in the service, the warm welcome and the consistency throughout.

Chef: **Bernd Wolf**. 3 course dinner from: **£28**. Seats: **42**

14-16 Parkhill Road, Torquay, Devon, TQ1 2AL.

T: 01803 213936
E: orangetreerestaurant@live.co.uk
www.orangetreerestaurant.co.uk

The Orange Tree Restaurant
@orangetreerest

100

The Horse

The Horse was transformed from a near derelict pub to a haven for foodies. Music, art and its own smoked deli delights complement an appealing restaurant at this buzzing hub. A bar with wooden floors, log fire and leather sofas serves award winning ales while the bright, flagstone-floored dining room overlooks a Mediterranean-style courtyard. As well as the popular Romanesque pizza and classic bistro dishes, try the speciality home-cured bresaola with pickled wild mushrooms.

Chef: **Christophe Ferraro**. 3 course lunch from: **£16**. 3 course dinner from: **£25**. Seats: **70**

7 George Street, Moretonhampstead, Devon, TQ13 8PG.

T: 01647 440242
E: info@thehorsedartmoor.co.uk
www.thehorsedartmoor.co.uk

The Horse [Moretonhampstead, UK]
@horsedartmoor

101 🔷
Ilsington Country House Hotel

Nestled in the picturesque surroundings of Dartmoor National Park, the Ilsington Country House Hotel is a beautiful spot for a foodie break, with a handful of awards under its belt. With the main restaurant overlooking Haytor and windows of the more informal bistro framed by rolling hills, there's beauty to be found inside and out of Ilsington. Chef Mike O'Donnell creates a lovely range of seasonally inspired dishes, and if you're staying for breakfast there's home-smoked salmon and freshly laid eggs to look forward to.

Chef: **Mike O'Donnell**. 3 course lunch from: **£21.50**. 3 course dinner from: **£36**. Seats: **50**. Bedrooms: **25**. Room rate from: **£120**

Ilsington, near Newton Abbot, Devon, TQ13 9RR.

T: 01364 661452
E: hotel@ilsington.co.uk
www.ilsington.co.uk

f Ilsington Country House Hotel
🐦 @ilsingtonhotel

102 🔷
The Royal Seven Stars Hotel

Located in the heart of Totnes and next to the River Dart, the award winning Royal Seven Stars Hotel offers a fabulous selection of fresh food, ales and wines. Led by head chef John Gallagher, the team of chefs prides itself on creating seasonal dishes that delight in using only the finest of locally sourced ingredients. Whether dining in one of the bars, out on the alfresco terrace or in the stylish TQ9 Brasserie, you can look forward to great service and inspired food.

Chef: **John Gallagher**. 3 course lunch from: **£22**. 3 course dinner from: **£27**. Seats: **35**. Bedrooms: **21**. Room rate from: **£125**

The Plains, Totnes, Devon, TQ9 5DD.

T: 01803 862125
E: enquiry@royalsevenstars.co.uk
www.royalsevenstars.co.uk

f Royal Seven Stars Hotel
🐦 @rsstotnes

103 🔷
The Grill Room

There's no missing the striking Royal Castle Hotel in Dartmouth. It's right on the inner harbour, with boats bobbing just a few feet away. It retains the historic grandeur that brought ships from across the world to this prosperous naval town. Enter through the old covered doorway and take the steps to The Grill Room, the hotel's first floor restaurant where menus are based on fresh seafood that's delivered daily and select cuts of locally raised meat. Led by head chef Ankur Biswas, this talented team creates stunning dishes that are vibrant in colour and taste.

Chef: **Ankur Biswas**. 3 course lunch from: **£19.50**. 3 course dinner from: **£25**. Seats: **60**. Bedrooms: **25**. Room rate from: **£160**

11 The Quay, Dartmouth, Devon, TQ6 9PS.

T: 01803 333033
E: enquiry@royalcastle.co.uk
www.royalcastle.co.uk

f Royal Castle Hotel
🐦 @rchdartmouth1

104
The Riverford Field Kitchen

Sit at wooden farmhouse tables and share platters piled high with veg straight from the farm in this innovative restaurant. At the heart of the Riverford organic veg box HQ, the field kitchen is housed in a stylish, modern barn where head chef Rob Andrews creams off some of the produce destined for boxes and turns it into an array of colourful, flavoursome dishes. The set menu includes a meat main and a veggie option. As everyone eats at the same time, booking is essential.

Chef: **Robert Andrews**. 3 course lunch from: **£23.50**. 3 course dinner from: **£27.50**. Seats: **72**

Wash Barn, Riverford Organic Farm, Buckfastleigh, Devon, TQ11 0JU.

T: 01803 762074
E: fieldkitchen@riverford.co.uk
www.riverford.co.uk/restaurant

f The Riverford Field Kitchen
🐦 @riverfordfk

DEVON

105 ❖

Plantation House Hotel and Restaurant

This intimate, characterful Georgian rectory impresses with its stylish, contemporary interior and well-proportioned bedrooms offering soothing rural views. Modern bathrooms come with heated floors, bathtubs, powerful showers and luxurious toiletries. Serious cooking from the chef/proprietor-led team is strong on flavour and texture, using exceptional and often homegrown ingredients. Plantation House is a destination for all seasons.

Chefs: **Richard Hendey and John Raines**. 3 course dinner from: **£36**. Seats: **26**. Bedrooms: **8**. Room rate from: **£95**

Totnes Road, Ermington, Ivybridge, Devon, PL21 9NS.

T: 01548 831100
E: info@plantationhousehotel.co.uk
www.www.plantationhousehotel.co.uk

 Plantation House Hotel

106

Barbican Kitchen

This funky, modern brasserie owned by the Tanner Brothers, Chris and James, is housed in the historic Plymouth Gin distillery. Enjoy classic, hearty dishes made with produce sourced from the bountiful West Country larder and served in the relaxed dining space with its own private dining room. Barbican Kitchen is open for lunch and dinner six days a week and is now the Tanner Brothers' main dining offering in Plymouth. Established in 2006, it caters for all – and kids under five eat for free. Go for fresh, local food at excellent prices.

Chefs: **Chris and James Tanner, Martyn Compton**. 3 course lunch from: **£15.95**. 3 course dinner from: **£15.95**. Seats: **100**

Plymouth Gin Distillery, 60 Southside Street, Plymouth, Devon, PL1 2LQ.

T: 01752 604448
E: info@barbicankitchen.com
www.barbicankitchen.com

 Barbican kitchen
 @barbicankitchen

107 ❖

Langdon Court Restaurant

Set in the South Hams countryside, this Grade II-listed 16th century manor house is just six miles from Plymouth and has welcomed notable guests in the last few hundred years, including Henry VIII and Elizabeth I. While steeped in history, the two AA rosette dining celebrates modern British cooking created by head chef Jamie Rogers who recently featured on *BBC Masterchef: The Professionals*. Visit to try his seasonal menus using produce that's often sourced within 20 miles of the hotel.

Chef: **Jamie Rogers**. 3 course brasserie lunch: **£20**. 3 course dinner from: **£35**. Seats: **40**. Bedrooms: **20**. Room rate from: **£129**

Adam's Lane, Down Thomas, Plymouth, Devon, PL9 0DY.

T: 01752 862358
E: enquiries@langdoncourt.com
www.langdoncourt.com

 Langdon Court Hotel & Restaurant
 @langdoncourtuk

108

Rhodes @ The Dome

Gary Rhodes brings a touch of foodie glam to a waterfront location on Plymouth's famous Hoe. Situated just below the iconic Smeaton's Tower, Rhodes @ The Dome is a striking building with a glass domed ceiling and the perfect vantage point looking out across Plymouth Sound. Contemporary and spacious inside it offers an appealing, bistro style menu alongside à la carte options. Enjoy a glass of wine or freshly made cocktails in the cool Bar Rhodes area.

Chef: **Paul Webber**. 3 course lunch from: **£22.50**. 3 course dinner from: **£22.50**. Seats: **140**

Plymouth Dome, Hoe Road, Plymouth, Devon, PL1 2NZ.

T: 01752 266600
E: info@rhodesatthedome.co.uk
www.rhodesatthedome.co.uk

 Rhodes at the Dome
 @rhodesdome

109

The Cornish Arms

Unpretentious food with hearty flavours is on the menu at this refurbished coaching inn in the heart of the Dartmoor town of Tavistock. Proprietors John and Emma Hooker took over in May 2013 with the aim of creating a pub they'd love to visit themselves. This year the pub won a prestigious Michelin Bib Gourmand and was placed 21st in the Top 50 Gastropub Awards 2015.

Chef: **John Hooker**. 3 course lunch from: **£19**. 3 course dinner from: **£25**. Seats: **48**

15 West Street, Tavistock, Devon, PL19 8AN.

T: 01822 612145
E: info@thecornisharmstavistock.co.uk

www.thecornisharmstavistock.co.uk

🟥 Cornish Arms
🟦 @cornisharmstavy

110 ◈

Hotel Endsleigh

A wonderful sense of history permeates Hotel Endsleigh. Built as a (rather grand) fishing lodge in 1810 by the Duke of Bedford, it's in a beautiful position in the Tamar Valley. Overlooking the curving river in the valley below, the Grade I-listed house is surrounded by landscaped gardens and woodland - complete with cascading water, follies and grottos. Food is locally sourced and modern English in style. With its crackling log fires in winter and alfresco dining in the natural landscape in summer, this is a hugely appealing countryside escape.

3 course lunch from: **£28**. 3 course dinner from: **£42.50**. Seats: **40**. Bedrooms: **17**. Room rate from: **£190**

Milton Abbot, Tavistock, Devon, PL19 0PQ.

T: 01822 870000
E: mail@hotelendsleigh.com

www.hotelendsleigh.com

🟥 Hotel Endsleigh
🟦 @hotelendsleigh

TRENCHERMAN'S ONLINE

On the web

Find the full list of restaurants, read the latest features and book online at many of the restaurants in the guide through **Bookatable** on the website:
www.trenchermans-guide.com

DEVON

On your tablet

Download the guide from **iTunes**, **Google Play** and **www.pocketmags.com**

Twitter and Facebook

Join the conversation on
Twitter: **@trenchermans**
Facebook: **The Trencherman's Guide**

CORNWALL

Let the salty sea air develop your appetite for some seriously good cooking created from exquisite local ingredients.

THE IDLE ROCKS p.111

Cornwall

111 Langmans Restaurant
112 The View Restaurant
113 Talland Bay Hotel
114 Asquiths
115 Q Restaurant at the Old Quay House Hotel
116 Restaurant Nathan Outlaw
117 Outlaw's
118 Paul Ainsworth at No. 6 in Padstow
119 The Seafood Restaurant
120 St Petroc's Bistro
121 Rick Stein's Cafe
122 The Cornish Arms
123 Zacry's
124 Jamie Oliver's Fifteen Cornwall
125 Tabb's Restaurant
126 The Quarterdeck at The Nare
127 The Idle Rocks
128 Pendennis Restaurant at The Royal Duchy Hotel
129 New Yard Restaurant
130 Mullion Cove Hotel
131 Kota
132 Roswarne Manor Restaurant
133 The Halsetown Inn
134 Ben's Cornish Kitchen
135 The Bay Restaurant
136 Harris's Restaurant
137 The Gurnard's Head
138 The Old Coastguard

139 The Springer Spaniel
140 Outlaw's Fish Kitchen
141 therestaurant@boscundle
142 The Carlyon Bay Hotel
143 The Restaurant at Trevalsa Court
144 Quies Restaurant at Treglos Hotel
145 St Moritz Hotel
146 The Watch House
147 Saffron
148 The Dining Room @ Rose in Vale
149 Samphire Bistro
150 The Ferryboat Inn
151 Housel Bay Hotel and Restaurant
152 The Victoria Inn
153 Tolcarne Inn
154 2 Fore Street Restaurant

New in the guide this year:

Zacry's, The Cornish Arms, Mullion Cove Hotel, New Yard Restaurant,
The Ferryboat Inn, therestaurant@boscundle, The Dining Room @ Rose in Vale.

Restaurants listed in the guide correspond to the numbers plotted on the map.
Locations are approximate.

111
Langmans Restaurant

INTIMATE DINING IN CALLINGTON

Chef Anton Buttery's passion for the art of cookery stands out a mile at this gem of a restaurant in the south east corner of Cornwall. Langmans has been wowing diners for 15 years, and this one-chef operation continues to draw in the accolades – winning the South West Tourism Silver Taste of the West Award and silver in the Visit Cornwall Awards this year alone. The tasting menus produced by Anton are faultless, beautifully constructed with delicate flavours that contrast and excite. The attention to detail goes right back to sourcing: Anton personally seeks out seasonal ingredients and has built up strong relationships with the suppliers he visits – from beef farms to cheese dairies. From the table linen to the cheeseboard, everything about dining here is perfectly executed, and with Anton's wife Gail on front of house, you'll also enjoy a very warm, genuine welcome.

Chef: **Anton Buttery**
7 course evening tasting menu: **£42.50, with optional flight of 7 wines £35**
Seats: **24**

3 Church Street, Callington, Cornwall, PL17 7RE.

T: 01579 384933
E: dine@langmansrestaurant.co.uk
www.langmansrestaurant.co.uk

 Langmans Restaurant
 @langmansdining

112
The View Restaurant

MODERN COOKING WITH STUNNING COASTAL VIEWS

The aptly named The View is perched high on the cliffs at Whitsand Bay, looking out across the stunning Rame Peninsula.
Chef Matt Corner has used his fine dining experience to create a relaxed experience with a simple, elegant menu in a vibrantly modern, family restaurant. The menu changes daily with fish and seafood taking centre stage in spring and summer, giving way to meat and game in the cooler months. This is simple food cooked precisely.

Chef: **Matt Corner**
3 course lunch from: **£28**
3 course dinner from: **£31**
Seats: **45**

Treninnow Cliff, Millbrook, Cornwall, PL10 1JY.

T: 01752 822345
E: root@theview-restaurant.co.uk
www.theview-restaurant.co.uk

113 ◈ ☐

Talland Bay Hotel

BLISSFUL COASTAL HIDEAWAY FOR FOODIES

Sublimely peaceful, the sheltered valley where you'll find Talland Bay Hotel is a beautiful spot to while away a few hours – or days. The hotel's surrounded by an award winning garden and has far reaching views out across the bay while, inside and out, there's quirky artwork to enjoy.

Chef Nick Hawke's appealing food in the two AA rosette Terrace Restaurant is traditional but imaginative, demonstrating a pleasing attention to detail. Pop in for a brasserie style lunch after exploring the South West Coast Path and nearby sandy beaches; visit for dinner or stay for a foodie getaway.

Chef: **Nick Hawke**
3 course lunch from: **£25**
3 course dinner from: **£42**
Seats: **40**
Bedrooms: **23**
Room rate from: **£125**

Porthallow, Looe, Cornwall, PL13 2JB.
T: 01503 272667
E: info@tallandbayhotel.co.uk
www.tallandbayhotel.co.uk

f Talland Bay Hotel
🐦 @tallandbayhotel

114

Asquiths Restaurant

FINE DINING IN LOSTWITHIEL

After a career which saw him cooking for royals and government ministers, chef Graham Cuthbertson moved to Cornwall where he opened his own restaurant with his wife Sally. Asquiths has won praise and awards for its confident and imaginative modern British menu – dishes such as pheasant ravioli and slow-cooked Cornish pork belly. Enjoy creative fine dining along with a relaxed vibe in the cosy dining room with its stone walls, white table linen and striking local artworks. Situated in the antique-hunters' paradise of Lostwithiel, Asquiths is a great find for quality dining.

Chef: **Graham Cuthbertson**
3 course dinner from: **£26**
Seats: **28**

19 North Street, Lostwithiel, Cornwall, PL22 0EF.
T: 01208 871714
E: info@asquithsrestaurant.co.uk.
www.asquithsrestaurant.co.uk

f Asquiths Restaurant
🐦 @asquiths_dining

115 $

Q Restaurant at the Old Quay House Hotel

MODERN CUISINE BY THE WATERSIDE

Make your way down the narrow streets of this charming Cornish town to find the Old Quay House, a boutique hotel with a rich history. Its waterside location, bright artwork and sunny terrace make it a quintessential slice of modern Cornwall. It's chic throughout, from the contemporary bedrooms to the hotel's Q Restaurant which, in warm weather, spills out on to a terrace. It's this prime location that's the big draw for dining while watching the coming and goings on the Fowey Estuary. The restaurant is open for lunch, afternoon snacks and dinner with chef Ben Bass's menus championing the best of West Country produce such as Fowey mussels and Creedy Carver duck. There's a strong wine list too.

Chef: **Ben Bass**
3 course lunch from: **£20**
3 course dinner from: **£37.50**
Seats: **30**
Bedrooms: **11**
Room rate from: **£190**

28 Fore Street, Fowey, Cornwall, PL23 1AQ.

T: **01726 833302**
E: **info@theoldquayhouse.com**
www.theoldquayhouse.com

f The Old Quay House Hotel
🐦 @theoldquayhouse

116

Restaurant Nathan Outlaw

NATHAN'S NEW PORT ISAAC MUST-VISIT

Newly relocated to Port Isaac from St Enodoc Hotel in Rock, Nathan's eponymous restaurant has been awarded two Michelin stars for the past four years. Its new, two-level setting captures stunning ocean views from the top of Port Isaac and features a main dining room upstairs and a chef's table downstairs. Fish and seafood is the star here and it's served exclusively in a tasting menu, showing off the bounty of the surrounding coastal waters. With prior notice, an increasingly popular vegetarian tasting menu can also be enjoyed. With Nathan in the kitchen most of the time, this is a truly memorable dining experience and a Cornish must-visit.

Chefs: **Nathan Outlaw and Chris Simpson**
Lunch and dinner tasting menu: **£99**
Lunch four course tasting menu: **£49**
Seats: **24 and chef's table of up to 12**

6 New Road, Port Isaac, Cornwall, PL29 3SB.

T: **01208 880896**
E: **mail@nathan-outlaw.com**
www.nathan-outlaw.com

🐦 @nathanoutlaw

THERE'S AN ADVENTURE BREWING

Sharp's 'There's an Adventure Brewing' campaign will give people the opportunity to win one of five extraordinary adventures during 2015.

The first adventure will offer members of the public the chance to join Sharp's Director of Brewing and world renowned brewer, Stuart Howe, on a journey to create their very own personal brew. Winners will join Stuart at the Sharp's brewery, where they'll learn the art of craft brewing, working through their own ideas to bring to life their perfect taste profile.

Their beer will be brewed and made available as a limited edition across select pubs and bars as well as the Sharp's shop.

To find out more go to — **www.sharpsadventure.co.uk**

ROCK • CORNWALL

TELEPHONE **01208 862 121**
VISIT **WWW.SHARPSBREWERY.CO.UK**
FOLLOW US 🇫 🐦   drinkaware.co.uk for the fort

117 ⬦

Outlaw's

**FABULOUS CASUAL DINING
IN ROCK**

This is a stunning place to enjoy Outlaw
inspired food in Cornwall, with an excellently
priced seasonal menu of three courses for
£45. Outlaw's is situated within the stylish
St Enodoc Hotel, and overlooks the Camel
Estuary, so in fine weather, diners are able
to take in the views from the sunny terrace.
The dining style is relaxed and easy-going
but with quality and Nathan's style running
throughout, including in the three course set
lunch menu for £25 that celebrates some of
the celeb chef's past and present favourites.
Local seafood and meats are complemented
by fresh vegetables, dairy and other produce
carefully sourced from the surrounding
Cornish countryside.

Chef: **Tom Brown**
3 course lunch from: **£25**
3 course dinner from: **£45**
Seats: **60**
Bedrooms:**20**
Room rate from: **£185**

St Enodoc Hotel, Rock Road, Rock,
Cornwall, PL27 6LA.

T: 01208 862737
E: info@outlaws.co.uk

www.outlaws.co.uk

f Outlaw's
🐦 @outlawsinrock

118 ☐

Paul Ainsworth at No. 6 in Padstow

**PLAYFUL, MICHELIN-STARRED
COOKING IN CORNWALL**

Paul Ainsworth at No. 6 is situated in an
intimate Georgian townhouse in the pretty
village of Padstow on the north Cornwall
coast. There's a warm welcome for guests,
who will be encouraged to have fun sampling
the innovative menu and eclectic wine list.
There's no dress code and the friendly team
just wants everyone to enjoy the experience
of dining at this exciting restaurant. Children
over the age of four are welcome, and
Paul and his team are always happy to
accommodate individual dietary needs.

Chef: **Paul Ainsworth**
3 course lunch from: **£25**
3 course dinner from: **£51**
Seats: **46**

6 Middle Street, Padstow, Cornwall,
PL28 8AP.

T: 01841 532093
E: enquiries@number6inpadstow.co.uk

www.number6inpadstow.co.uk

f Paul Ainsworth at Number 6
🐦 @no6padstow

119 $

The Seafood Restaurant

FRESH FISH AT RICK'S PLACE

This much loved restaurant opened in 1975 and is still the main hub of Rick Stein and Jill Stein's businesses in Padstow. Fresh oysters, langoustines, mussels, turbot, dover sole, lobster and sashimi are all on the menu, which includes dishes inspired by Rick's travels. You can also sit at the seafood bar in the middle of the stylish restaurant and watch the chefs prepare shellfish while enjoying a dish or two from the menu. An extensive wine list is carefully selected by Rick and his team of sommeliers.

Chef: **Stephane Delourme**
3 course lunch from: **£31**
3 course dinner from: **£40.90**
Seats: **130**
Bedrooms:**16 (and an additional 6 in St Edmund's House)**
Room rate from: **£154**

Riverside, Padstow, Cornwall, PL28 8BY.

T: **01841 532700**
E: **reservations@rickstein.com**
www.rickstein.com

 Rick and Jill Stein - The Seafood
@theseafood

120 $

St Petroc's Bistro

RELAXED BISTRO AND BOUTIQUE HOTEL FROM THE STEIN TEAM

Classic bistro dishes, including some of Rick Stein's favourite Mediterranean dishes, are a central theme at this vibrant restaurant. St Petroc's is the fifth oldest building in Padstow and has a comfortable atmosphere with its low beams, winding stairs and fireplaces. There's a good selection of well-aged steaks and simply grilled fish such as plaice, sea bass and lemon sole. The snug bar and lounge are perfect for pre- or post-dinner drinks.

Chef: **Nick Evans**
3 course lunch from: **£25**
3 course dinner from: **£29**
Seats: **50**
Bedrooms:**10 (and an additional 4 in Prospect House)**
Room rate from: **£160**

4 New Street, Padstow, Cornwall, PL28 8EA.

T: **01841 532700**
E: **reservations@rickstein.com**
www.rickstein.com

 Rick and Jill Stein - The Seafood
@theseafood

121 ⬥

Rick Stein's Cafe

EASY-GOING GLOBAL FOOD IN AN INFORMAL SETTING

This hugely popular cafe is open daily, serving freshly cooked breakfasts, light lunches and relaxed dinners. Simple seafood dishes and imaginative flavours rule here and the menu changes daily. Thai, Moroccan and the Med influence the cooking, so you could find moules mariniere, pad thai noodles and deep fried sea bass with chilli sauce and cashew nuts on the menu. With options like Cornish ribeye steak, and lamb and spinach karahi curry, there are plenty of non-fish alternatives, and the informal setting is perfect for families.

Chef: **Mark O'Hagan**
3 course lunch from: **£23.50**
3 course dinner from: **£23.50**
Seats: **36**
Bedrooms:**3**
Room rate from: **£113**

Middle Street, Padstow, Cornwall, PL28 8AP.

T: 01841 532700
E: reservations@rickstein.com

www.rickstein.com

Rick and Jill Stein - The Seafood
@theseafood

122

The Cornish Arms

RICK STEIN'S CLASSIC CORNISH PUB

Tuck into real beef burgers, mussels and chips and good old scampi in the basket at this country pub which is one of Rick Stein's restaurants. It's a showcase for his recipes, which are created on a daily basis by head chef Alex Clark. Menus comprise of simple British pub dishes, along with an authentic drinks selection, including some of St Austell Brewery's best ales and a great choice of wines. Exposed stonework, beams and wooden tables create a relaxed, rustic vibe and there's a large beer garden in which to relax during the warmer months. Kids and well behaved dogs are welcome and the chilled out vibe means you could end up staying for hours.

Chef: **Alex Clark**
3 course lunch from: **£24.50**
3 course dinner from: **£24.50**
Seats: **270**

Churchtown, St Merryn, Cornwall, PL28 8ND.

T: 01841 532700
E: reservations@rickstein.com

www.rickstein.com

Cornish Arms
@thecornisharms

Q RESTAURANT p.103

123 💲
Zacry's

LAID-BACK AMERICAN-STYLE CUISINE BY THE BEACH

With its floor to ceiling windows overlooking Watergate Bay and cool, split level seating arrangement, Zacry's is a perfect place to indulge in some post-beachtime relaxed dining. It's the latest additon to the dining options at Watergate Bay Hotel and, under the guidance of executive chef Neil Haydock, holds true to the hotel's ethos of using fresh Cornish produce in the creative, brasserie style menu. Zacry's draws on international influences and a passion for contemporary American cuisine, with a menu that showcases both classical and contemporary dishes. Expect big, bold meat and seafood flavours from the indoor charcoal oven. The lobster is a must!

Chef: **Carl Paparone**
2 course evening menu from: **£29.50**
3 course evening menu from: **£36.50**
Seats: **120**
Bedrooms: **69**
Room rate from: **£135**

124
Jamie Oliver's Fifteen Cornwall

FUNKY, FEEL-GOOD RESTAURANT WITH STUNNING VIEWS

Overlooking Watergate Bay, this is a spectacular spot for breakfast, lunch or dinner. Watch surfers compete for waves or sit back and take in a glorious Cornish sunset through the restaurant's vast picture windows. Chef Andy Appleton delights in creating Italian inspired, rustic, honest food using mindfully sourced, quality assured, seasonal ingredients. Each dish tells a story, educating the senses and enriching the experience. The restaurant is home to the Cornwall Food Foundation, an independent registered charity, with all profits going towards its apprentice programme which trains young adults from Cornwall to be the chefs of the future.

Chef: **Andy Appleton**
3 course lunch from: **£32**
3 course dinner from: **£48**
Seats: **120**

DEVON

Watergate Bay Hotel, Watergate Bay, Cornwall, TR8 4AA.
T: **01637 861231**
E: **eat@zacrys.com**
www.zacrys.com
f Zacry's
🐦 @zacryswgb

On the beach, Watergate Bay, Cornwall, TR8 4AA.
T: **01637 861000**
E: **reservations@fifteencornwall.co.uk**
www.fifteencornwall.co.uk
f Fifteen Cornwall
🐦 @fifteencornwall

125

Tabb's Restaurant

QUALITY DINING IN CORNWALL'S CAPITAL CITY

Soft lilac colours and simple slate floors provide the perfect setting for Nigel Tabb's simple, modern dishes. Intimate and understated is the theme at this contemporary eatery that used to be a pub. London-trained Nigel has developed a loyal following for his two AA rosette restaurant in Cornwall's capital city. Every dish is carefully considered, drawing on Nigel's expertise, so expect to be charmed by little touches including perfectly baked bread and divine handmade chocolates. You'll probably want to sample everything made by Nigel, so make the most of the £12 Tabb's Tapas taster menu at lunchtime, in addition to the set menu.

Chef: **Nigel Tabb**
3 course lunch from: **£25**
3 course dinner from: **£25**
Seats: **30**

85 Kenwyn Street, Truro, Cornwall, TR1 3BZ.
T: **01872 262110**
E: **info@tabbs.co.uk**
www.tabbs.co.uk

Tabb's Restaurant
@nigeltabb

126 ◈

The Quarterdeck at The Nare

LIFE ON THE OCEAN WAVES AT CARNE BEACH

The sea is always within reach when you dine at The Quarterdeck. Whether you decide to eat inside or move out onto the large terrace, there are glorious views across Gerran's Bay. The Quarterdeck is the relaxed, informal restaurant at The Nare hotel on the Roseland Peninsula. Open throughout the day, from morning coffee through to à la carte evening dining, it's a light-filled space with a coastal inspired yachting theme. The fabulous array of seafood dishes to choose from emphasises chef Richard James' passion for using local produce. Fish and shellfish may be star choices, but the steaks from locally reared beef attract an equally large following. An extensive wine cellar completes the pleasing culinary experience.

Chef: **Richard James**
3 course lunch from: **£27**
3 course dinner from: **£35**
Seats: **60**
Bedrooms: **37**
Room rate from: **£270**

Carne Beach, Veryan, Truro, Cornwall, TR2 5PF.
T: **01872 500000**
E: **reservations@narehotel.co.uk**
www.quarterdeckrestaurant.co.uk

@thenarehotel

127 ⑤

The Idle Rocks

STYLISH SETTING IN ST MAWES

The Idle Rocks is idyllically situated on the Harbourside of St Mawes. With 19 bedrooms (each uniquely designed), a restaurant with views across the unspoilt harbour and a south-facing terrace that perches perfectly on the rocks, this is a place to re-engage with life's simple pleasures.

Enjoy a vibrant menu showcasing the best Cornish ingredients, prepared with simplicity and flair and served with tranquil views across the water.

Chef: **Mark Apsey**
3 course lunch from: **£35**
3 course dinner from: **£45**
Seats: **65**
Bedrooms:**19**
Room rate from: **£195**

Harbourside, St Mawes, Cornwall,
TR2 5AN.
T: 01326 270270
E: info@idlerocks.com
www.idlerocks.com

f The Idle Rocks
y @theidlerocks

128 ⑤

Pendennis Restaurant at the Royal Duchy Hotel

MODERN BRITISH CUISINE IN FALMOUTH

The beautiful Pendennis Restaurant is the epitome of classic British style. Situated at the heart of the four-star Royal Duchy Hotel in Falmouth, which enjoys stunning views of the bay. The recent high-spec refurbishment of the restaurant is matched by seriously good, two AA rosette standard dining from head chef John Mijatovic and team. Expect to encounter a warm, friendly welcome at this elegant, foodie escape.

Chef: **John Mijatovic**
3 course lunch from: **£20**
3 course dinner from: **£35**
Seats: **100**
Bedrooms:**43**
Room rate from: **£70**

Cliff Road, Falmouth, Cornwall,
TR11 4NX.
T: 01326 313042
E: reservations@royalduchy.com
www.royalduchy.com

f The Royal Duchy Hotel
y @brendhotels

CORNWALL

JAMIE OLIVER'S FIFTEEN CORNWALL p.109

129
New Yard Restaurant

RELAXED, ECO-FRIENDLY DINING

This relaxed restaurant in the 1000-year-old Trelowarren Estate near Helston is hugely popular with food lovers – at all times of the day. The attractive, chilled out setting, friendly team and good cooking sees it busy from morning to night as foodies visit for rustic lunchtime sustenance and high quality evening dining. The green credentials of the estate are echoed in the provenance of the ingredients, with game from the estate and fish and shellfish coming from local dayboats.

Chef: **Chris Philliskirk**
3 course lunch from: **£25**
3 course dinner from: **£25**
Seats: **45**

Trelowarren, Mawgan, Helston, Cornwall, TR12 6AF.
T: 01326 221595
E: newyard@trelowarren.com
www.trelowarren.com

☐ Trelowarren New Yard Restaurant
☐ @newyardcornwall

130 ⬥
Mullion Cove Hotel

EXCEPTIONAL COOKING IN A CLASSIC CORNISH HOTEL

This wonderful Cornish hotel high up on the cliffs above Mullion Harbour has long been recognised as one of the county's finest. And with talented Kiwi head chef Fiona Were in situ, the experience goes from strength to strength. Her two AA rosette cuisine uses fresh, local and seasonal produce to create playful, thoughtfully produced dishes with an international twist. It's seen her recognised as one of the top ten female chefs in the UK, and the food is just one of many very good reasons for visiting this charming seaside retreat.

Chef: **Fiona Were**
3 course lunch from: **£18**
3 course dinner from: **£35**
Seats: **60**
Bedrooms:**30**
Room rate from: **£95**

Mullion Cove, Lizard Peninsula, Helston, Cornwall, TR12 7EP.
T: 01326 240328
E: enquiries@mullion-cove.co.uk
www.mullion-cove.co.uk

☐ Mullion Cove Hotel
☐ @mullioncove

131 $

Kota

CORNISH PRODUCE WITH A KIWI KICK ON THE HARBOURSIDE

There's superb seafood and organic produce to be discovered at this much-loved Cornish restaurant with rooms. Chef owner Jude Kereama is a New Zealander ('Kota' is Maori for shellfish) who arrived in Cornwall ten years ago, having run restaurants in London and Auckland. Jude's menu uses the best Cornish produce to which he adds his signature Asian twist. The food is complemented by a choice of over 90 wines from around the world. Located right on the harbour front at Porthleven, this atmospheric seaside restaurant with a rustic but spacious interior has two AA rosettes, and has held a Michelin Bib Gourmand for two years.

Chef: **Jude Kereama**
3 course set dinner: **£21.50**
Seats: **32**
Bedrooms: **2**
Room rate from: **£30 per person per night**

Harbour Head, Porthleven, Cornwall, TR13 9JA.
T: **01326 562407**
E: **kota@btconnect.com**
www.kotarestaurant.co.uk

 Kota
 @kota_kai

132 $

Rosewarne Manor Restaurant

SHOWCASE DINING IN FAMILY-OWNED MANOR HOUSE

Great attention to detail pervades this 1920s manor house which is owned and run by the Eustice family, who have renovated it to a modern standard. Their efforts have paid off, and it's a great showcase for Rosewarne's long-time chef Phil Thomas' two AA rosette à la carte menu. Not far from the beach at Hayle, it also has its own lovely gardens to enjoy. Visit for the special tasting menu on the last Thursday of each month or dig into the informal menu which offers simpler versions of the fine dining dinner classics.

Chef: **Phil Thomas**
3 course lunch from: **£19**
3 course dinner from: **£30**
Seats: **36**
Bedrooms: **1**
Room rate from: **£90**

Gwinear Road, Connor Downs, Hayle, Cornwall, TR27 5JQ.
T: **01209 610414**
E: **enquiries@rosewarnemanor.co.uk**
www.rosewarnemanor.co.uk

 Rosewarne Manor Restaurant & function venue
 @rosewarnemanor

133
The Halsetown Inn

GLOBAL INFLUENCES IN CREATIVE PUB MENU

Step within the granite walls of this old flagstone floored pub and you'll find a team that is passionate about producing top quality food, and also about the whole dining experience. It opened three years ago up the hill from its sister venture, Blas Burgerworks, and in that time has gained a loyal following. Aussie chef, Ange Baxter, brings individuality and fun to the medley of affordable dishes and there's an excellent choice for vegetarians. Pub faves include fantastic curries such as red duck curry with green mango and pear salad; beetroot bourguignon and the Halsetown Jaffa Cake. Globally inspired in flavours, a "keep it local" sustainable message permeates the entire operation – even the electricity is 100 per cent renewable, coming from a local hydro-electric dam. There are also plans to renovate its letting rooms this year.

Chef: **Ange Baxter**
3 course lunch from: **£15**
3 course dinner from: **£22**
Seats: **80**

Halsetown, St Ives, Cornwall, TR26 3NA.
T: **01736 795583**
E: **info@halsetowninn.co.uk**
www.halsetowninn.co.uk

f Halsetown Inn
🐦 @halsetowninn

134 ☐
Ben's Cornish Kitchen

FAMILY RUN BISTRO WITH STAR QUALITY

Just across the road from the sea – and the striking St Michael's Mount, Ben's Cornish Kitchen makes full use of its coastal setting. With its simple white stone walls and wooden floors, this relaxed, bistro-style restaurant has a highly accomplished and award winning chef at its helm. Ben Prior leads the small team (almost all are family members) and the dedication to his culinary art and welcoming, accessible approach is paying dividends, including recently being awarded a second AA rosette. This is a hugely popular foodie haunt, with diners coming back again and again to sample Ben's inspired dishes, which consistently excite and satisfy. Be prepared for a few surprises, not least of which is the modest pricing including a personally chosen wine list that starts from £16.

Chef: **Ben Prior**
3 course lunch from: **£20**
3 course dinner from: **£26**
Seats: **40**

West End, Marazion, Cornwall, TR17 0EL.
T: **01736 719200**
E: **ben@benscornishkitchen.com**
www.benscornishkitchen.com

f Ben's Cornish Kitchen
🐦 @cornishkitchen

THE HALSETOWN INN p.115

135 ⬧

The Bay Restaurant

HEAVENLY VIEWS AND FOOD IN PENZANCE

Overlooking the characterful fishing town of Penzance, The Bay Restaurant is a little slice of heavenly calm. Tasteful, comfortable and modern, the décor includes local artwork to complement the panoramic views of Mounts Bay. A skilled team led by chef Ben Reeve is behind two AA rosette The Bay with its fresh and diverse menu. The hotel restaurant provides all day dining, so you can pop in for fresh and simple lunches, a delightful afternoon tea or an early supper after work – or, in warm weather, take the time to relax over the à la carte evening selection on the terrace.

Chef: **Ben Reeve**
3 course lunch from: **£28**
3 course dinner from: **£28**
Seats: **40**
Bedrooms: **25**
Room rate from: **£80**

Hotel Penzance, Britons Hill, Penzance, Cornwall, TR18 3AE.

T: **01736 363117**
E: **eat@thebaypenzance.co.uk**
www.thebaypenzance.co.uk

◼ The Bay Restaurant
◼ @perfectpenzance

136

Harris's Restaurant

INTIMATE DINING EXPERIENCE IN PENZANCE

This boutique restaurant has been on the foodie trail for many years, with its beautifully cooked fish and seafood sourced from Falmouth and Newlyn Fish Market, and locally reared lamb and beef. To complete the dining experience, the wine list is extensive and exciting, and chef Roger Harris's desserts are a must. Lunches are served upstairs in the bar restaurant and dinner is served downstairs. The à la carte menu is available for lunch and dinner – one, two or three courses, the choice is yours.

Chef: **Roger Harris**
3 course lunch from: **£27.50**
3 course dinner from: **£27.50**
Seats: **20 in the restaurant, 20 in the bar**

46 New Street, Penzance, Cornwall, TR18 2LZ.

T: **01736 364408**
E: **contact@harrissrestaurant.co.uk**
www.harrissrestaurant.co.uk

SEASONAL SPECIALITY COFFEE. SOURCED DIRECTLY.

We source our coffee directly from growers to ensure an exceptional product which is ethical and sustainable. We roast in Cornwall on a Loring Smart Roast, the world's first environmentally friendly roaster. Our coffee is roasted lightly to enhance the individual characteristics that the growers have worked tirelessly to perfect.

Experience Origin at leading independent coffee shops & boutique hotels. Or buy via our website.

origincoffee.co.uk

ORiGiN ®
coffee roasters

137 ◈
The Gurnard's Head

**A GOURMET RETREAT IN THE WILDS
OF CORNWALL**

On the stunning north coast of Cornwall,
between St Ives and St Just, surrounded
by moorland and the breathtaking coastal
path, The Gurnard's Head is a retreat for
body and soul.

New head chef Jack Clayton's food is spirited
and strong on flavours, coaxing the very best
out of the region's locally produced ingredients
– and the wine choice is excellent too. Seven
bedrooms with vibrantly coloured décor,
antique furniture and Vi-Spring beds offer
a place for relaxation after a day's walking.
Children and dogs are also both welcome to
eat and stay. On the south coast, you'll find the
Gurnard's sister hotel, The Old Coastguard.

Chef: **Jack Clayton**
3 course lunch from: **£19**
3 course dinner from: **£26**
Seats: **70**
Bedrooms: **7**
Room rate from: **£110**

Zennor, St Ives, Cornwall, TR26 3DE.

T: 01736 796928
E: enquiries@gurnardshead.co.uk

www.gurnardshead.co.uk

❋ The Gurnard's Head
❋ @gurnardshead

138 ◈
The Old Coastguard

**CONTEMPORARY CORNISH
EXPERIENCE IN MOUSEHOLE**

Enjoy eating simple, well-executed food that
celebrates the rhythm of the seasons and the
coastal landscape at this seaside hotel in the
fishing village of Mousehole.

Matt Smith, who has returned as head chef,
creates high quality food that diners can dig
into in the dining room, in the bar or, in
summer, outside on the terrace with its views
of the tropical gardens.

The Old Coastguard is under the same
ownership as the popular Gurnard's Head,
across the moor in Zennor. The welcome is
warm and the team friendly, making the
environment as relaxing as the bedrooms,
which nearly all look out over glistening
Cornish inland waters. Children and dogs are
very welcome too.

Chef: **Matt Smith**
3 course lunch from: **£17.50**
3 course dinner from: **£23.50**
Seats: **80**
Bedrooms: **14**
Room rate from: **£130**

The Parade, Mousehole, Penzance,
Cornwall, TR19 6PR.

T: 01736 731222
E: enquiries@oldcoastguardhotel.co.uk

www.oldcoastguardhotel.co.uk

❋ The Old Coastguard
❋ @leroundhouse

CORNWALL

CORNWALL

139
The Springer Spaniel

A successful mix of appealing pub food and more ambitious dining makes The Springer Spaniel a place to return to time and again. Always a popular pub, it was taken over by former *BBC MasterChef: The Professionals* winner, Anton Piotrowski (who holds a Michelin star at The Treby Arms), and given a fresh new look and menu. It shares the laid-back, community pub vibe of its sister pub, along with the superb food and excellent service. The Springer team sets out to inspire with its friendly approach and passion for British food with provenance.

Chefs: **Anton Piotrowski and Ali Fraser**.
3 course lunch from: **£20**. 3 course dinner from: **£22**. Seats: **60**

Treburley, Launceston, Cornwall, PL15 9NS.

T: 01579 370424
E: enquiries@thespringerspaniel.org.uk
www.thespringerspaniel.co.uk

f The Springer Spaniel
🐦 @springerthe

140
Outlaw's Fish Kitchen

Opened by Nathan Outlaw in 2013, the 15th century fisherman's cottage turned restaurant overlooks the harbour in Port Isaac. Relaxed dining is the order of the day at this little restaurant, and the menu is dictated by what's landed each day. The catch is turned into small, unique and delicious seafood plates, all cooked to order. Choose as few or as many dishes as you like while taking in the vibrant atmosphere of the lively fishing village. Be aware though, during lunch it's first come, first served and it's a popular spot.

Chef: **Simon Davies**. Selection of plates for lunch and dinner from: **£6-£14**. Seats: **24**

1 Middle Street, Port Isaac, Cornwall, PL29 3RH.

T: 01208 881183
E: fishkitchen@outlaws.co.uk
www.outlaws.co.uk/fishkitchen

f Outlaw's Fish Kitchen
🐦 @fish_kitchen

141 ⚡

therestaurant@boscundle

This charming manor house consistently serves excellent, modern British two AA rosette food that's exquisitely stylish. The culinary team is passionate about serving dishes brimming with the finest seasonal ingredients, sourced wherever possible from the South West. With an ambience to match, the dining room provides an intimate, candle-lit setting in which to savour the fine food and wine, alongside a carnival of fresh flowers and beautiful glassware. A bright and airy conservatory offers a more relaxed setting.

Chef: **Adam Gerrish**. 3 course lunch from: **£29**. 3 course dinner from: **£29**. Seats: **24 (parties up to 46)**. Bedrooms: **14**. Room rate from: **£99**

Boscundle Manor, Boscundle, St Austell, Cornwall, PL25 3RL.

T: 01726 813557
E: reservations@boscundlemanor.co.uk

www.boscundlemanor.co.uk

f Boscundle Manor
🐦 @boscundlemanor

142 ⚡

The Carlyon Bay Hotel

Cornwall's original four star hotel, this 1930s ivy-clad building has unique panoramic views over St Austell Bay. In the last year the restaurant has benefited from a six figure refurbishment so the inside is as beautiful as those views of the stunning Cornish seascape. Chef Paul Leakey uses local quality ingredients to create menus which have brought the hotel an AA rosette. Dine in the elegant restaurant, or for a more creative, playful gastronomic experience head to the Taste Brasserie at the front of the hotel.

Chef: **Paul Leakey**. 3 course lunch from: **£18.50**. 3 course dinner from: **£38**. Seats: **220**. Bedrooms: **86**. Room rate from: **£75**

Sea Road, St Austell, Cornwall, PL25 3RD.

T: 01726 812304
E: reservations@carlyonbay.com

www.carlyonbay.com

f The Carlyon Bay Hotel
🐦 @carlyonbayhotel

143 ⚡

The Restaurant at Trevalsa Court Hotel

With picturesque views over the rugged Cornish coastline, it's easy to see why so many return to Trevalsa Court Hotel. The interior of the handsome old granite house pairs ancient oak panels with arty décor to create a warm and welcoming atmosphere. The menu, crafted by chef Adam Cawood, is small but perfectly formed, with quirky touches at each course, such as rhubarb pasta for dessert. Expect to discover quality, local produce in a relaxed and informal setting.

Chef: **Adam Cawood**. 3 course lunch from: **£20**. 3 course dinner from: **£30**. Seats: **30**. Bedrooms: **15**. Room rate from: **£70**

School Hill, Mevagissey, Cornwall, PL26 6TH.

T: 01726 842468
E: stay@trevalsa-hotel.co.uk

www.trevalsa-hotel.co.uk

f Trevalsa Court Hotel and Restaurant
🐦 @trevalsacourt

144 ⚡ ☐

Quies Restaurant at Treglos Hotel

With stunning sea views across Constantine Bay, Quies Restaurant has an enviable home within Treglos Hotel. The family run hotel has been in the hands of the Barlow family for over 40 years and their decades of hard work are reflected in the confident service. The large restaurant is open throughout the day for laid-back lunches and afternoon teas, and by evening there's a smart but relaxed atmosphere with elegant food to match. Look forward to plenty of fresh Cornish produce on a menu that changes by the day.

Chef: **Gavin Hill**. 3 course dinner from: **£34**. Seats: **85**. Bedrooms: **42**. Room rate from: **£147**

Treglos Hotel, Beach Road, Constantine Bay, Cornwall, PL28 8JH.

T: 01841 520727
E: stay@tregloshotel.com

www.tregloshotel.com

f Treglos Hotel
🐦 @tregloshotel

TRENCHERMAN'S
AWARDS

**BEST DINE AND
STAY EXPERIENCE**
2015

145
St Moritz Hotel

MODERN EUROPEAN FOOD
IN A COOL SEASIDE SETTING

This contemporary and stylish hotel on the north Cornish coast has a vibrant open kitchen where you can watch the talented team of chefs at work. Head chef Jamie Porter has worked under some of the country's biggest names and brings brilliantly executed modern European cooking to this cool seaside setting. Fresh local ingredients, particularly seafood, shine through – from Camel Estuary lobster to Porthilly oysters and even fish caught on Jamie's dad's own boat. Dine in the elegant hotel restaurant or the relaxed poolside cafe, Sea Side.

Chef: **Jamie Porter**. 3 course lunch from: **£25**. 3 course dinner from: **£40**. Seats: **50**.
Bedrooms: **48**. Room rate from: **£120**

Trebetherick, Wadebridge, Cornwall, PL27 6SD.
T: 01208 862242
E: reception@stmoritzhotel.co.uk
www.stmoritzhotel.co.uk

f St Moritz Hotel Cornwall
y @stmoritzhotel

CORNWALL

146

The Watch House

The old Customs and Excise watch house and pilchard press in the heart of the fishing village of St Mawes is now a bustling bistro restaurant that's popular with locals and tourists alike. Chef owner Will Gould creates lively menus of food you want to eat by the sea packed with fresh Cornish produce, including dayboat fish specials. Eat downstairs in a group-friendly dining booth or upstairs in the bright restaurant with views across the harbour out to St Anthony Head. The Watch House also sells MSC certified fish with hand-cut double cooked chips and local ice cream to take away.

Chef: **Will Gould**. 3 course lunch from: **£25**. 3 course dinner from: **£35**. Seats: **65**

1 The Square, St Mawes, Cornwall, TR2 5DJ.

T: 01326 270038
E: info@watchhousestmawes.co.uk
www.watchhousestmawes.co.uk

The Watch House
@the_watch_house

147

Saffron

A champion for Cornish food, head chef Nik Tinney can always be found in the local markets, sourcing items for his menus. For over ten years, this friendly restaurant in the heart of Truro has been at the forefront of the Cornish food revival. Nik's menus are always changing, depending on what produce he and the team have uncovered. A refurbishment reflects the restaurant's fine dining credentials, but it remains a relaxing and welcoming place to eat. You'll find a stylish bar, cosy candlelit booths and a wood burner. The pre-theatre set menu is especially excellent value.

Chef: **Nik Tinney**. 3 course lunch from: **£20**. 3 course dinner from: **£30**. Seats: **45**

5 Quay Street, Truro, Cornwall, TR1 2HB.

T: 01872 263771
E: reservations@saffronrestauranttruro.co.uk
www.saffronrestauranttruro.co.uk

Saffron Truro
@saffrontruro

148 ⊛

The Dining Room @ Rose in Vale

Enjoy elegant yet relaxed dining at the restaurant of this four star Cornish hotel in the village of Mithian. The family owned Georgian property has been carefully renovated by owners James and Sara Evans and has impressive green credentials. No surprise then that the food at The Dining Room is locally sourced and seasonal. A team of young chefs who have come to work at the hotel following apprenticeships at Rick Stein's and Fifteen Cornwall, have brought vitality and inspiration to the menus - leading to a two rosette rating within weeks.

Chef: **James Bennets**. 3 course lunch from: **£19.95**. 3 course dinner from: **£34**. Seats: **40**. Bedrooms: **22**. Room rate from: **£140**

Rose in Vale, Mithian, St Agnes, Cornwall, TR5 0QD.

T: 01872 552700
E: bookatable@thediningroom.co
www.thediningroom.co

Rose in Vale Country House Hotel
@_thediningroom_

149

Samphire Bistro

With a kitchen bursting with local Cornish produce, a trip to Samphire in the centre of Falmouth is a must for visitors to the historic town. From freshly caught fish, to the Camel Valley wine, the French bistro style menus are a nod to the abundance of quality produce from Cornwall's fields and waters and everything is cooked with class and care. Drawing on a mix of Asian and Mediterranean influences, chef Dave Trewin creates unfussy yet distinctive dishes. Open for lunch in the summer and dinner all year round – the five course tasting menu is particularly intriguing.

Chef: **Dave Trewin**. 3 course lunch from: **£15**. 3 course dinner from: **£25**. Seats: **50**

36 Arwenack Street, Falmouth, Cornwall, TR11 3JF.

T: 01326 210759
E: info@samphire-falmouth.co.uk
www.samphire-falmouth.co.uk

Samphire Restaurant
@samphirefal

PENDENNIS RESTAURANT p.111

150
The Ferryboat Inn

Set course for excellent food at this laid-back setting in an enviable location on the riverbank of the North Helford Passage. The Ferryboat Inn is a 300-year-old pub that welcomes all the family, including four-legged friends. Crafting a small but well-rounded menu of British dishes, chef Robert Bunny lives by his farm-to-fork philosophy, so expect fine fresh vegetables and the best of the Cornish shores - including oysters from the inn's own oyster farm just along the river.

Chef: **Robert Bunny**. 3 course lunch from: **£20**. 3 course dinner from: **£25**. Seats: **60**

Helford Passage, Helford, Cornwall, TR11 5LB.

T: 01326 250625
E: reservations.ferryboat@thewrightbrothers.co.uk

www.wrightbrothers.co.uk

The Ferryboat Inn
@wbferryboatinn

151 ⬡
Housel Bay Hotel and Restaurant

If you wanted to find a spot for dinner with a view in Cornwall, then you'd be hard pushed to beat Housel Bay. It's a grand old hotel set high on the cliffs at The Lizard - one of the county's most dramatic coastal locations. The hotel has achieved an AA rosette for the standard of its food for four years in a row. Dishes are always interesting, featuring fresh ideas and with almost everything made on the premises. Sit back and enjoy while gazing at that view out to the lighthouse and across the ocean. Open for breakfast, lunch and dinner, seven days a week.

3 course lunch from: **£25**. 3 course dinner from: **£35**. Seats: **50**. Bedrooms: **21**. Room rate from: **£99**

The Lizard, Helston, Cornwall, TR12 7PG.

T: 01326 290417
E: info@houselbay.com

www.houselbay.com

Housel Bay Hotel
@houselbayhotel

152 ⬡
The Victoria Inn

Reputedly one of the oldest inns in Cornwall the Victoria Inn is in the little village of Perranuthnoe in the far west of Cornwall. Behind its unassuming exterior you'll find a multi-award winning food offering based on modern Cornish cuisine. It also boasts an excellent selection of fine wines and local ales. The Victoria Inn retains a Cornish character and charm that has earned it a loyal following, both from locals and visitors to the area. It's perfect for cosy winter dining by the fire or enjoying lazy summer afternoons in the enclosed terrace garden.

Chef: **Nik Boyle**. 3 course lunch from: **£25**. 3 course dinner from: **£25**. Seats: **60**. Bedrooms: **2**. Room rate from: **£75**

Perranuthnoe, Penzance, Cornwall, TR20 9NP.

T: 01736 710309
E: enquiries@victoriainn-perranuthnoe.co.uk

www.victoriainn-penzance.co.uk

Victoria Inn Perranuthnoe
@victoriaperran

TRENCHERMAN'S ONLINE

Twitter and Facebook

Join the conversation on
Twitter: **@trenchermans**
Facebook: **The Trencherman's Guide**

INTEGRITY
PASSION
AUTHENTICITY

The South West's must-have food and drink guides

Coming soon!

NORTH OF ENGLAND SPECIALITY COFFEE GUIDE
SOUTH WEST CRAFT BEER GUIDE

www.saltmedia.co.uk
www.food-mag.co.uk

153
Tolcarne Inn

Chef Ben Tunnicliffe set out on a mission to serve affordable, accessible food at this 18th century pub in the fishing village of Newlyn. Three years in, and with a Michelin Bib Gourmand, he's achieved it, and also just opened a second beachside restaurant at Sennen Cove. For Ben, good food is about seasonality and quality ingredients – which he's a master at, having built up strong relationships with suppliers over 15 years. With Newlyn fish market a stone's throw away, seafood's a speciality at the Tolcarne - and live jazz on Sunday afternoons is a bonus.

Chef: **Ben Tunnicliffe**. 3 course lunch from: **£26**. 3 course dinner from: **£28**. Seats: **40**

Tolcarne Place, Newlyn, Penzance, Cornwall, TR18 5PR.

T: 01736 363074
E: info@tolcarneinn.co.uk
www.tolcarneinn.co.uk

f Tolcarne Inn
🐦 @ben_tunnicliffe

154
2 Fore Street Restaurant

It's not surprising this busy little harbourside bistro in Mousehole is as popular with locals as it is with holidaymakers. 2 Fore Street is open all day so you can enjoy it in many different ways – from a coffee in the pretty, secluded garden, to lingering over supper with a chilled glass of prosecco. Literally a stone's throw from the sea, the menu is predominantly fish and seafood based and changes according to what's been landed that day.
Chef Joe Wardell, who trained under Raymond Blanc, has a simple, unfussy style and his cooking is grounded in classic cuisine.

Chef: **Joe Wardell**. 3 course lunch from: **£20**. 3 course dinner from: **£28**. Seats: **36**

2 Fore Street, Mousehole, Penzance, Cornwall, TR19 6PF.

T: 01736 731164
www.2forestreet.co.uk

INSIDER'S TIP

'Gidleigh Park (p 83) is amazing of course, and I also like to go to The Two Bridges Hotel (p 85). Its chef Mike Palmer is passionate about what he's doing and this is reflected in the food.'

CORNWALL

Ben Prior of Ben's Cornish Kitchen. Page 115.

INDEX

	Page
2 Fore Street Restaurant	127
ABode Exeter	81
Acorn Inn	69
Arbor Restaurant	71
Arundell Arms Hotel Hotel and Restaurant, The	90
Asquiths	102
Augustus	58
Barbican Kitchen	96
The Bath Priory	46
The Bay Restaurant	117
Beaminster Brasserie at the BridgeHouse	66
The Bell at Ramsbury	37
Ben's Cornish Kitchen	115
Best Western Plus Centurion Hotel	60
Best Western The Grange at Oborne	65
Bird in Hand	45
Brasserie at Lucknam Park Hotel & Spa	37
Captains Club Hotel and Spa	69
The Carlyon Bay Hotel	121
Cary Arms	82
Casamia	43
The Castle at Taunton	58
The Castle Inn Hotel	36
The Coach House by MichaelCaines	75
Combe House Devon	77
The Cornish Arms (St Merryn)	107
The Cornish Arms (Tavistock)	97
Crab House Café	71
The Daffodil Restaurant	26
The Dartmoor Inn	87
The Dining Room @ Rose in Vale	123
The Ferryboat Inn	125
The Fontmell	68
The Fox at Broughton Gifford	38
The Foxham Inn	36
The Galley Restaurant	94
The George & Dragon	35
Gidleigh Park	83
The Globe	61
Goodfellows	55
Graze Bar, Brewery and Chophouse	51
The Grill Room	95
The Gurnard's Head	119
The Halsetown Inn	115
Harris's Restaurant	117
The Harrow at Little Bedwyn	33
The Hartnoll Hotel	93
Highcliff Grill Restaurant	67
Hix Oyster and Fish House	69
The Horn of Plenty	90

The Horse	94	The Restaurant at Trevalsa Court	121
Hotel Endsleigh	97	Restaurant Nathan Outlaw	103
Housel Bay Hotel and Restaurant	125	Rhodes @ the Dome	96
Howard's House	39	Rick Stein's Cafe	107
Idle Rocks Hotel	111	The Rising Sun Inn	61
Ilsington Country House Hotel	95	The Riverford Field Kitchen	95
Jamie Oliver's Fifteen Cornwall	109	Riverside Restaurant	66
The Kensington Arms	50	The Riviera Hotel and Restaurant	78
Kota	114	Rock Salt Cafe Brasserie	91
La Petite Maison	79	Rodean Restaurant	94
Langdon Court Restaurant	96	Ronnie's of Thornbury	43
Langmans Restaurant	101	Roswarne Manor	114
The Lazy Toad Inn	93	The Royal Seven Stars Hotel	95
Les Saveurs at The Seafood Restaurant	79	The Rusty Bike	93
Lewtrenchard Manor	87	Saffron Bistro	123
Little Barwick House	59	The Salty Monk	78
The Longs Arms	39	The Salutation Inn	93
Lower Slaughter Manor	23	Samphire	123
Lucknam Park Hotel and Spa	32	Saunton Sands Hotel	76
Lumière	24	The Seafood Restaurant	106
The Magdalen Chapter	81	Second Floor Restaurant and Bar	44
The Manor House	31	The Slaughters Country Inn	23
mark@street	26	Soar Mill Cove Hotel	86
The Masons Arms	76	The Springer Spaniel	120
Menu Gordon Jones	47	St Moritz Hotel	122
The Methuen Arms	32	St Petroc's Bistro	106
The Miners Country Inn	27	The Stapleton Arms	68
The Mint Room	51	Swan, The (Bampton)	77
Muddy Duck	37	Swan, The (Wedmore)	55
Mullion Cove Hotel	113	Tabb's Restaurant	110
New Yard Restaurant	113	Talland Bay Hotel	102
Northcote Manor Country House Hotel	92	therestaurant@boscundle	121
The The Northey Arms	37	The Three Daggers	39
The The Old Coastguard	119	The Three Gables	35
The Olive Tree Restaurant	46	The Three Lions	65
The Orange Tree Restaurant	94	Tolcarne Inn	127
Outlaw's	105	The Treby Arms	89
Outlaw's Fish Kitchen	120	The Two Bridges Hotel	85
Paul Ainsworth at No. 6 in Padstow	105	The Victoria Inn	125
Pear Tree at Purton	31	The View Restaurant	101
The Pendennis Restaurant at the Royal Duchy Hotel	111	The Watch House	123
The Pilgrims Restaurant	56	Waterside Bistro	82
Plantation House Hotel and Restaurant	96	Watersmeet Hotel	75
The Pony And Trap	49	WestBeach	69
Prego	50	The Wheatsheaf Combe Hay	49
Prince Hall Hotel and Restaurant	85	Wheelwrights Arms	51
Psalter's Restaurant at The Luttrell Arms	60	The White Hart	56
The Pump House	45	The White Horse	61
Q Restaurant at the Old Quay House	103	Wild Garlic Restaurant	24
The Quarterdeck at The Nare	110	Wilks Restaurant	44
The Queens Arms	59	Yeoldon House Hotel	92
Quies Restaurant at Treglos Hotel	121	Zacry's	109